CONTENTS

CHAIRMAN AND MEMBERS OF THE HEALTH AND SAFETY COMMISSION 1999/2000

Chairman

Sir Frank Davies CBE OStJ became Chairman of the Health and Safety Commission on 1 October 1993. He has over 40 years of experience of working in industry including construction, aluminium and glass manufacturing. He was Chief Executive of Rockwear Group plc between 1983 and 1993 and is past-President of the European Glass Federation. He is non Executive Director of Aggregate Industries plc and Saltire plc. He is Vice-President of St John Ambulance in Oxfordshire. He is Companion of the Institute of Management, Vice-President of the Institute of Packaging and Honorary Vice-President of the Institute of Occupational Safety and Health.

Commissioners

Mr George Brumwell. Appointment commenced on 1 April 1998. He is General Secretary of the Union of Construction, Allied Trades and Technicians. He is a member of the Labour Party National Policy Forum and the TUC's Executive Committee and General Council. He is a long-time member of the construction Industry Training Board and a board member of the Construction Skills Certification Scheme for the Construction Industry. He is an Executive Committee Member of the European and International Federation of Building and Wood Unions.

Ms Margaret Burns. Appointment commenced on 1 April 1998. She is a part-time tutor of Public Law at the University of Aberdeen. She has taught in the law faculties at Dundee and Glasgow Universities and at the Open University. She was formally the Legal Advisory Officer for, and is now a member of, the Scottish Consumer Council, which nominated her for the Health and Safety Commission.

Mr David Coulston. Appointment commenced on 29 November 1996. He is Director of Health, Safety and Environment with British Nuclear Fuels Ltd. He has over 25 years experience as a health and safety professional within industry and represents the interests of employers on the Commission. He has served on a number of national and international bodies including the European Union's Science and Technology Committee, senior health and safety committees within the Confederation of British Industry and the Chemicals Industry Association and two of the Commission's advisory committees. He led the Engineering Sector Task Group assisting the Commission in its review of regulation. Mr Coulston resigned from the Commission on 31 March 1999.

Cllr Joyce Edmond-Smith. Appointment commenced on 1 April 1997. She has been a councillor for 13 years and is a member of Brighton and Hove Council. She has been a member of the Association of District Councils for eight years and has a wide experience of environmental and health issues in local government. Over the past ten years she has chaired the Brighton Environment and Planning Committee and the Environment and Health Committee of the Association of District Councils. She has been a member of Brighton and Hove Community Health Council and is presently a member of the 'Local Agenda 21' Steering Committee. She taught in further education for 20 years.

Mr Alan Grant. Appointment commenced on 1 April 1995. He is head of the TUC Organisation and Services Department, which includes responsibility for health and safety policy. He has been a TUC official since 1978, initially working on health and safety training, and was previously Head of the TUC Trade Union Education Department. He formerly worked in the printing industry before gaining an MA in industrial relations. Mr Grant resigned from the Commission on 13 November 1998.

Ms Anne Gibson OBE. Appointment commenced on 1 April 1996. She is National Secretary of the Manufacturing Science and Finance Union with responsibilities for policy and political work of the union and is a member of the TUC General Council. She is the TUC spokesperson on health and safety issues at national and international level. She was formally an Equal Opportunities Commissioner and a member of the Women's National Commission.

Dr Mike McKiernan. Appointment commenced on 1 April 1996. He is Director of Health, Safety and Environmental Projects at TRW Inc. (previously LucasVarity plc). He was nominated for the Commission by the Engineering Employers' Federation (EEF) and was the Chairman of the EEF's Occupational Health Committee. He is an accredited specialist in occupational medicine and has over 20 years of experience as a health and safety practitioner. He also has experience of working with small and medium-sized enterprises.

Mr Rex Symons CBE. Appointment commenced on 1 October 1989. He acts as the CBI workplace health and safety consultant and is Chairman of its Health and Safety Committee. He is a member of the Employment National Training Organisation and Chairman of Poole Hospital NHS Trust. He is also Chairman of Bournemouth Transport Ltd and Dorset Travel Services Ltd. He was Chairman of Dorset Training and Enterprise Council for six years until 1998 and Deputy Chairman of Merck Holdings from 1989 to 1991 and Managing Director of BDH Chemicals Ltd (formally British Drug Houses Ltd) from 1980 to 1989. He is a member of the Employment Tribunals. He is also a Governor of the Bournemouth Arts Institute.

Mr Owen Tudor. Appointment commenced on 17 November 1998. He is a Senior Policy Officer at the TUC responsible for health and safety and legal services. He was a member of the HSC Advisory Committee on Toxic Substances and Occupational Health Advisory Committee's occupational health services sub-group. He is the Secretary to the National Occupational Health Forum and the TUC Rehabilitation Initiative Steering Committee. He also holds two other public appointments, he is a member of the Industrial Injuries Advisory Council and a member of the Civil Justice Council.

Mr Robin Turney. Appointment commenced on 1 April 1997. He has extensive experience of the chemical industry where he has held management positions both in the UK and abroad. He is currently a consultant on safety, health and environment issues with special interest in hazard identification, management systems and auditing, on which he has both written and lectured. He has been Chairman of the Institution of Chemical Engineers' Loss Prevention Panel since 1996. He also represents the UK on the European Federation of Chemical Engineers' Safety Loss Prevention Working Party. Mr Turney resigned from the Commission on 31 March 1999.

New members from 1 April 1999

Mr Abdul Chowdry JP. Appointment commenced on 1 April 1999. He gained more than 34 years experience as a Health, Safety and Environment Advisor at Turner and Newall plc (manufacturing), where he worked until August 1998. He is the Director of Blackburn/Darwen Racial Equality Council. He has been a magistrate since 1976. He was a Labour Councillor at Rochdale Metropolitan Borough Council from 1972 to 1998, where he chaired a number of committees including Housing, Policy and Economic Development. He was also a member of the Greater Manchester Police Authority from 1986 to 1998.

Mr Sonny Hamid. Appointment commenced 1 April 1999. He commenced his training in electrical engineering in 1954. In 1969 his career led him into fire engineering and he gained membership of the Institution of Fire Engineers. His career path developed to include senior fire engineering, environmental health and safety and engineering and construction positions at Foster Wheeler Petroleum Development Ltd, Bechtel GB Ltd and Bechtel inc. Following the acquisition of Trafalgar House by Kvaerner plc in 1996, he has been actively engaged in preparing and implementing a new environmental, health and safety policy in the group companies, serving clients in six main industrial sectors world-wide.

MEMBERS OF THE HEALTH AND SAFETY EXECUTIVE

Director General   **Jenny Bacon CB**

Director General since 1995, Jenny Bacon joined HSE as Deputy Director General in March 1992. She gained wide public experience in a variety of posts in the Department of Employment (including preparing the Health and Safety at Work etc Act 1974; the Manpower Services Commission; the Cabinet Office; and the Department of Education and Science).

Deputy Director General   **David Eves CB**

David Eves is responsible for the work of HSE's operational divisions. He was appointed Deputy Director General and made a member of the Executive in 1989 following a year as Director of Resources and Planning. Prior to this he held the post of Chief Inspector of Factories between 1985-1988 having joined HM Factory Inspectorate in 1964.

Director, Resources and Planning Directorate   **Richard Hillier**

Richard Hillier was appointed to the Executive in 1996. He joined HSE in 1994, having previously worked in the Employment Department on pay and industrial relations policy, equal opportunities, health and safety, and overseas labour. He also led the Manpower Services Commission's work on training and enterprise strategy, following spells in the field of technical and vocational education, and employment policy.

HSE STRUCTURE

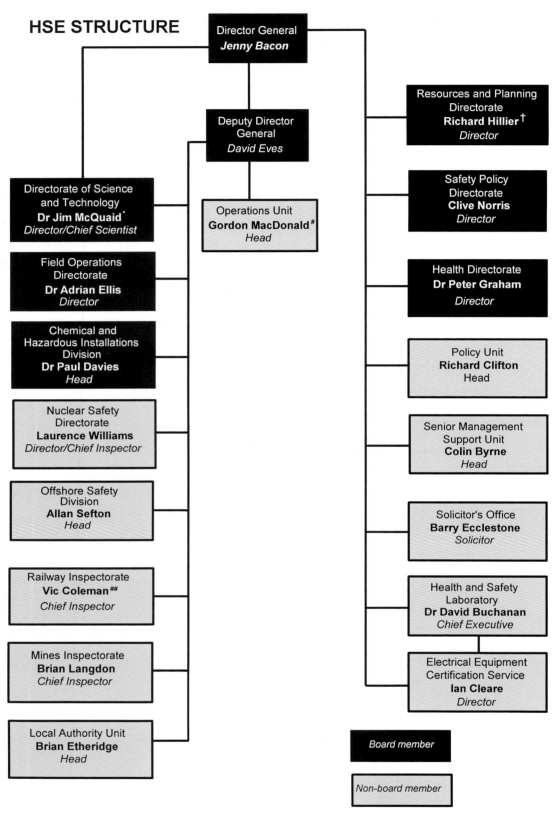

Director General
Jenny Bacon

Deputy Director General
David Eves

Directorate of Science and Technology
Dr Jim McQuaid[*]
Director/Chief Scientist

Field Operations Directorate
Dr Adrian Ellis
Director

Chemical and Hazardous Installations Division
Dr Paul Davies
Head

Nuclear Safety Directorate
Laurence Williams
Director/Chief Inspector

Offshore Safety Division
Allan Sefton
Head

Railway Inspectorate
Vic Coleman[##]
Chief Inspector

Mines Inspectorate
Brian Langdon
Chief Inspector

Local Authority Unit
Brian Etheridge
Head

Operations Unit
Gordon MacDonald[#]
Head

Resources and Planning Directorate
Richard Hillier[†]
Director

Safety Policy Directorate
Clive Norris
Director

Health Directorate
Dr Peter Graham
Director

Policy Unit
Richard Clifton
Head

Senior Management Support Unit
Colin Byrne
Head

Solicitor's Office
Barry Ecclestone
Solicitor

Health and Safety Laboratory
Dr David Buchanan
Chief Executive

Electrical Equipment Certification Service
Ian Cleare
Director

Board member

Non-board member

* Director, Directorate of Science and Technology reports to Director General as Chief Scientist
† Richard Hillier sits on the Board as third member of the Executive
# Gordon MacDonald took over from David Ashton as head of Operations Unit on 2 November 1998
Vic Coleman took up post on 14 July 1998 following the retirement of Stan Robertson on 13 July 1998

Chairman's Foreword

This is my last Annual Report as Chairman of the Health and Safety Commission. I leave with regret. Having worked in every continent except for Antarctica, and in four very different industries, I have found the last six years with the Commission to be among the most interesting and enjoyable of my career. The pleasure of working with such a wide range of dedicated, hard working, and knowledgeable people has been a major part of this. And dealing with two different Governments, six different Ministers and three different departments of state during those six years has certainly added to the spice of life.

I would like to pay particular tribute to the Commission. I am regularly surprised and pleased at their wide range of competencies; they are from many and varied walks of life and all bring these valuable experiences to their work. During the last six years I have chaired 130 Commission meetings, dealing with over 700 items. We have never once failed to reach agreement or been forced to take a vote. This is a huge tribute to the determination of the Commission members to work together in the best spirit of Robens.

Reflecting on my time as Chairman, amongst the many issues I've had to deal with, there are a number of themes which predominate. And looking at this year's Annual Report, these are issues which will continue to be important for HSC and HSE.

Better and more effective regulation

The Review of Regulations, because it was initially labelled as deregulation, caused a huge amount of controversy. But by picking up on the Robens idea of regular review of regulations to remove outdated legislation we were able to get the agreement of everyone involved, and get rid of 40% of regulations. We have continued to simplify and modernise regulations and improve the quality of our guidance.

Fragmentation of industry

The increasing fragmentation of industry is probably the most worrying development we face. For HSC, which which makes considerable efforts to consult widely - this fragmentation, along with the lack of union representation of many workers, means that the number and range of those we are consulting is reducing. Who else is there for instance, with the knowledge, representative nature and commitment of the TUC? This will be an increasing challenge in the years ahead.

The ever increasing number of small businesses - 3.7 million at the last count - means that direct contact by inspectors is impossible. We have to find other ways of reaching small firms and their workers - and I am talking here about working through and in partnership with others. This has been a priority for us during the year and will continue to be in the future.

Small firms have been a particular concern of mine as Chairman. Through the Commission's small firms breakfast meetings and our consultation exercise in 1996 I have worked hard to find out what they want and ensure that we do our best to provide it. Most tell me they want straightforward, practical help. The Good Neighbours Scheme is proving to be a valuable way of providing this - and one which is dependent on the efforts of others for its success. We also published guidance aimed specifically at small firms, and carried out a range of initiatives to reach small firms.

The injury and ill health record

I am pleased to report that the estimated figure for the number of workers fatally injured in 1998/99 looks like being one of the lowest on record. Deaths are expected to fall from 274 in 1997/98 to 257. These figures are early estimates, so there could be some adjustment. But there are clear downwards trends in the numbers and rates of fatal injury to workers over the last ten years. The non-fatal major injury rates for employees and the self-employed have also fallen. But I believe we are now getting to the difficult core and hitting the law of diminishing returns.

We have, I think, made some progress in construction - deaths to construction workers are estimated to fall by 14, although the major injury rate for construction workers is expected to show a rise of 8%. But I see little progress in agriculture, where the fatal injury rate for workers is expected to rise because of the increase of ten in the number of injuries to the self-employed. The rise in the number of fatal injuries in the manufacturing industry, estimated to be the highest this decade, is of particular concern to me. The most noticeable increases have been in the manufacture of basic metals and fabricated metal products and in recycling.

For several kinds of occupational disease, including hearing loss, upper limb disorders and dermatitis, the numbers of cases assessed for compensation by the Department of Social Security have continued to fall in recent years. The latest figures for asthma also show some signs of falling.

Asbestos continues to be the main cause of fatal occupational illness, though because of the long time intervals between exposure and death, typically twenty years or more, the latest figures reflect the working conditions of the past. Deaths from mesothelioma, nearly all probably caused by asbestos, increased by 2% in 1997, following a slight fall in 1996, thus showing a lower rate of increase to that seen earlier, there having been an 8% annual average increase in the decade up to 1995.

Occupational health

In 1996 the Commission moved occupational health to the top of our agenda, with campaigns such as Good Health is Good Business, and it remains there. An estimated two million people believe they suffer ill health caused by their work each year. Latest estimates show the total costs to society of work-related ill health to be up to some £11 billion. I have said many times before that the humanitarian reason for improving health and safety should be enough - but for the doubters the economic case is unanswerable. The third phase of our Good Health is Good Business campaign focused on solvents and hand-arm vibration. It was supported by guidance, publicity initiatives, conferences and inspection initiatives targeted at specific sectors of industry. HSE's audits of employers' performance on the management of specific health risks indicate that we are having some success in getting the message of managing health risks across - but there is still more to be done.

On asbestos, after consultation, we have recommended draft regulations to the Secretary of State, effectively prohibiting the importation of white asbestos into the UK. We are under no illusion that this will show up in the statistics for many years yet, but believe it is the right action to take for the future.

We asked the Executive to prepare a ten year view for occupational health. They have conducted a very open and wide consultation and are reporting to us this summer. We have contributed to the public health agenda in England, Wales and Scotland. The workplace is a significant way of promoting wider public health objectives and we will be able to provide influence in workplaces across the country. We were particularly pleased to sign a joint Statement of Intent with the Department of Health, signaling our joint approach to improving public health, reflected in the Healthy Workplace Initiative.

Local authorities

I would like to congratulate warmly everyone involved in enforcement of health and safety in the local authority enforced sector for contributing so positively to the Commission's aims and objectives over the last year. Full details of the local authorities' work is given in HELA Annual Report 1999, published in July. Local authorities have responsibility for enforcement in 1.2 million premises and are an essential partner in our work on health and safety. I have worked hard at improving our relationship and think it fair to say that during my six years, the Commission, Executive and local authorities have moved from a position of some mistrust to one of mutual respect and understanding.

Resources

It was a great tribute to the importance of our work, and that we deliver value for money, that the Government authorised a significant increase in our budget in last year's Comprehensive Spending Review - much of this increase has to be covered by receipts from an extension of charging to the regulations of the offshore, rail and gas transportation industries and the COMAH regime. This will be a major challenge; there are risks to our relationship with those in industry.

I have no doubt that there are challenging times ahead, and believe that HSC/E is in good shape to meet them. I wish the next Chairman every success and hope he gets as much satisfaction and enjoyment from the job as I have had.

Sir Frank Davies CBE, OStJ

Director General's Foreword

Introduction

It has, once again, been a demanding but stimulating year. I am indebted to the commitment and hard work of HSE staff, and the enthusiasm and efforts of those in industry and elsewhere who have worked with us during the year. Together, I believe we are developing a firm basis for an effective health and safety system able to respond to the changes which have already happened in the labour market and society, and fit to meet the future challenges which lie ahead.

Working with others

Consultation and partnerships, working with and through others, are key elements of an effective approach. Improved health, safety and working environments for workers, stronger protection of and reassurance to the public, and assistance to industrial competitiveness require well targeted regulatory and support interventions. We need strong partnerships to improve targeting and the effectiveness of our interventions.

The year offered some good examples of what can be done. We combined with the environment agencies in a new competent authority to enforce the new Control of Major Accident Hazards Regulations - a major enterprise in joined up government. We have worked closely with the Department of Health to develop the Healthy Workplace Initiative, part of our contribution to Our Healthier Nation. Trades Unions, employers' associations, Chambers of Commerce, major employers, including local authorities, and others, have worked with us to make the Good Health is Good Business and Good Neighbour Forums initiatives successful and to develop industry specific campaigns. And we began the process of consulting widely with our stakeholders on the Commission's new three year Strategic Plan and on the development of a 10 year strategy for occupational health.

But we recognise that, to be truly successful in developing effective partnerships, we must be prepared to work to other people's agendas. Such power sharing does not come easily to an expert regulatory organisation. But genuine partnership means meeting the aims of all parties involved - even if not immediately relevant to our own.

Outreach and equality of access

We in HSE are convinced that good health is good business and that a sound working environment increases productivity and competitiveness. So we want everyone, irrespective of facts such as geography, size of firm, employment status, to have access to a good working environment, to adequate information and training, to trade union representation and so on.

The difficulties in achieving this are well known, and there are no easy solutions. We have worked hard over the years to find ways of reaching out to small and medium-size firms (SMEs), micro firms and to workers. This year, for example, we developed initiatives to improve our relationship with business support organisations; we worked with local occupational health and safety groups; we began a major project to find ways of providing occupational health support to SMEs. Our enquiry service - InfoLine - took 222 000 calls, about half from SMEs. We put all our free information on our web site - which already attracts over 75 000 hits a week - a total which grows each week. We held a safety representative conference and are encouraging the sharing of good practice on workforce involvement.

But there is much more to be done, particularly at local level. It is here that effective partnership can provide the most benefit.

The front line

The bedrock of our activity remains the work of our field forces. Their contacts with employers and workers - to give advice and where necessary to take formal action - are a powerful impetus to improved standards of health and safety. During the year, we made 183 000 regulatory contacts, exceeding our target; 78% of inspector time was spent in direct contact with clients and related activities; and 79% of planned inspections were to small firms. But we are victims of our own success in raising the profile of health and safety. We receive more complaints about working conditions each year (29 500 this year, 7000 more than we had forecast) so this year we could investigate only 80% of them. The challenge is a perennial one: how should we best use our resources - information, advice, guidance, inspection, investigation of accidents and complaints, enforcement action etc to make the most effective interventions - in today's diverse, complex and distributed labour market and in the context of today's societal expectations?

The accident record

We, and of course those responsible in industry, can take some credit from the reduction in the number of fatal injuries to workers and in the non-fatal major injury rates for employees and the self-employed. But we cannot relax our efforts. During the year, in response to previous years' figures, we carried out major programmes of work in the construction, agriculture and manufacturing sectors. There has been some improvement. But the fatal injuries to the self-employed in agriculture and the rate of non-fatal injuries to construction employees indicates we still have some way to go before our actions really start to bite. And it is disappointing that the traditional safety and health concerns - slips, trips, falls from heights, vehicle movements, dermatitis, lung disease and musculo-skeletal damage - recur with depressing predictability, across industries and occupations. This year we began a three year targeted campaign aimed at reducing transport related injuries in work places. If it is successful, there may be lessons we can apply to other areas.

Management and staff development

All parts of HSE have now gained recognition as Investors in People - a demonstration of commitment to the training and development of our staff and a tribute to the staff themselves. I am also pleased to record that our internal health and safety record has improved and that our major and over three day injury incidence rates are about one fifth the estimated national rates for office-based activities.

Efficiency and effectiveness

We continued our wide ranging programme of efficiency and business improvement work. This contributed to quantified efficiency gains of over £5 million - 3% of our running costs: a considerable achievement but slightly below target, reflecting the progressively more demanding nature of the task of identifying scope for efficiency. The development of HSE's business improvement programme should enable us to meet that challenge.

There is still much to do if we are to help people in industry to ensure not just that risks to health and safety are properly controlled, but also that working environments are improved so as to reduce labour market inequalities and increase productivity and competitiveness. But with the support and commitment of our partners, I am confident we can run a health and safety system which responds to changes and continues to lead the world.

Jenny Bacon CB

HSC/E'S MISSION STATEMENT

To ensure that risks to people's health and safety from work activities are properly controlled

Our key priorities for 1998/99:

- To promote occupational health and encourage improved management of health risks arising from work affecting both workers and the public.

- To improve health and safety at work by promoting the full participation of principal stakeholders - employers, employees and their representatives - and key intermediaries.

- To cut injury rates, particularly in the agriculture, construction and manufacturing sectors, especially by influencing duty holders through regulatory contacts, including preventive inspection.

- To take forward HSC's strategy for reaching small firms.

- To establish a regulatory regime which will address the control of major accident hazards into the next century.

Our continuing aims:

- To modernise, simplify and support the regulatory framework, including European Union and other international work.

- To secure compliance with the law in line with the principles of proportionality, consistency, transparency and targeting on a risk-related basis.

- To improve the knowledge and understanding of health and safety through the provision of appropriate and timely information and advice.

- To promote risk assessment and technological knowledge as the basis for setting standards and guiding enforcement activities.

- To operate statutory schemes, including regulatory services, through, for example, the Employment Medical Advisory Service.

- To maintain an efficient and effective central service which promotes and secures value for money.

Part 1

HEALTH AND SAFETY COMMISSION
ANNUAL REPORT 1998/99

Section 1

How we performed against our key priorities for 1998/99

Key priority for 1998/99: To promote occupational health and encourage improved management of health risks arising from work affecting both workers and the public

Better management of health risks arising from work

1.1   The 1995 Self-reported Work-related illness Survey (SWI95) found that some two million people suffer from illness caused by their work, resulting in the loss of around 18 million working days. A study based on the SWI 95 estimates that work-related ill health costs society between £6.2 - £7.2 billion in costs incurred in 1995/96. This increases to between £10.2 - £10.6 billion in present value terms, when also including estimates of future costs. Our approach is to encourage better management of health risks and to help employers get on top of health problems in their own workplaces, by providing them with simple and practical advice and guidance.

Third phase of the Good Health is Good Business campaign

1.2   We know that employers find health risks more difficult to manage than safety, and this prompted our Good Health is Good Business campaign (GHGB), a long-term programme first launched in May 1995 to help bring about changes in the way health risks are managed. From the outset this campaign has been a long-term programme which seeks to raise awareness of occupational health and improve employers' competence in managing health risks at work. The overriding objective is to reduce the unacceptable incidence of work-related illness. The third phase of the campaign focused on **solvents and hand-arm vibration (HAV)**. It remains a key priority for the Health and Safety Commission/Executive (HSC/E) and local authorities and has been fully supported by Ministers. The launch of the third phase also supported the key occupational health theme of the UK Presidency of the EU.

1.3   Phase three of the campaign was launched nationally (London, Cardiff and Edinburgh) on 22 May 1998. The launch was supported by the publication of a revised campaign guide for employers *Good health is good business guide*, leaflets on HAV for employers and employees, and on solvents for managers, safety representatives and employees; a video on HAV; and revised guidance on noise. Since the start of the campaign in 1995, we have distributed nearly 600 000 campaign management packs; issued more than 8000 copies of the *Make health your business* video; sold 700 copies of *Rash decisions*; nearly 600 copies of *Hard to handle*; and 900 copies of *Matter of life and breath* .

1.4   HSE has continued to promote the campaign through some media advertising, including special supplements in the Financial Times and the health and safety press; publicity initiatives; and through a wide range of field activities, many of which were organised in partnership with intermediaries such as the TUC and the British Chambers of Commerce. The campaign was also promoted during the 1998 European Week for Safety and Health.

1.5   Regulatory contacts included:

- 215 visits to premises in the polymers and fibres, engineering and utilities sectors, working with **solvents,** which resulted in enforcement action at 15-20% of visits; and a structured survey of solvent exposures in the footwear industry;

- a campaign to secure improved management of health risks associated with **HAV** in the foundries, engineering and utilities sectors. The campaign succeeded in raising awareness of HSE's guidance and enforcement notices were issued at 7% of the visits;

- a programme of visits to premises in the explosives industry, working with **solvents,** to evaluate the control of and take action to secure compliance where necessary - 72 visits were made resulting in 20 enforcement notices; and

- an inspection project on the management of **HAV** offshore. This showed that the use of vibrating tools is greater than was thought and that controls on HAVneed to be improved. The industry is introducing low-vibration equipment and inspectors will re-examine HAV issues during future inspections.

Evaluation of the campaign

1.6   This campaign is the largest ever run by HSE and it is important therefore that we establish its effectiveness in changing employers' behaviour and attitudes towards the management of health risks. An in-depth survey to evaluate the overall impact of the campaign commenced in March and the results will be available next year. Following two earlier media surveys which took account of multimedia advertising (including television and radio) awareness levels had more than doubled (from 21% to 54%). However, latest research has indicated a falling off in awareness, a reflection of the more limited advertising in 1998. Further research will allow future data comparisons to be made.

1.7   HSE undertook inspection audits of employers' performance in the management of specific health risks. The findings indicated that in broad terms, the message of managing health risks was getting across to employers, but that further attention was needed in the areas of monitoring and reassessing risks.

Asbestos

1.8   Asbestos continues to be the largest single cause of work-related fatal illness. Although the current annual death toll, estimated at around 3000, is a result of exposure several decades ago when exposure was less well controlled, HSC has been determined to strengthen regulatory control and to provide better protection for workers. During the year there were major developments.

- HSC consulted on amendment regulations to the Asbestos (Licensing) Regulations 1983 and the Control of Asbestos at Work Regulations 1987, and two related Advisory Codes of Practice (ACOPs) in April 1998. The Regulations and ACOPs came into effect in February 1999. A series of one-day road shows were organised jointly with the British Occupational Hygiene Society (BOHS) to promote the Regulations. In addition, new guidance was prepared and issued on the duty to use safer substitutes where these are available.

- As part of the April 1998 consultation, HSC sought views on the principle of further regulatory duties on those in control of places of work to identify and manage the risks from asbestos. Consultation demonstrated broad support for the proposals and further detailed consultation on regulatory duties, and an ACOP is planned for September 1999. Some slippage in the planned programme has arisen because of the high level of interest in our proposals and the complexity of drafting legislation that will be both effective and enforceable.

- HSC also consulted in September 1998 on proposals to further restrict the importation, supply and use of white asbestos. This consultation exercise showed overwhelming support for a domestic ban. As a result, HSC agreed in May 1999 to recommend draft regulations to the Secretary of State. These regulations will effectively prohibit the importation of white asbestos into the United Kingdom and its supply and use within Great Britain, with the exception of certain specialised areas of use, where there is no suitable substitute yet available. This work was carried out while we were also pressing for a European-wide ban on white asbestos (See paragraph 1.80).

- A national programme of inspection visits to asbestos removal operations, to improve the control of risks from asbestos removal operations and to promote the progressive elimination of dry stripping, hot work and the use of power tools - 894 visits were made and some 278 contractors were visited, representing 38% of those licensed.

- Inspectors made 47 visits (exceeding their target of 40) to local authorities to secure compliance with requirements relating to the management of risks from asbestos to maintenance and building workers in local authority property, in particular housing estates, leisure and education departments.

- Contacts were made to all manufacturers and suppliers of commercial heavy vehicles to secure the fitting of non-asbestos brake linings.

A new public health strategy

1.9   Public health initiatives concern preventing ill health generally and promoting good health. HSE's work on occupational health is primarily focused on preventing ill health caused or made worse by work. It is important therefore that HSE's work is closely co-ordinated with work on the broader public agenda, not least because the work place is one setting for promoting broader public health messages.

1.10   During the year we worked closely with the Department of Health (DOH), Scottish Office and Welsh Office to ensure occupational health considerations feature (or will feature) in public health White Papers and framework documents. In particular, we worked closely with the Department of Health to develop the Healthy Workplace Initiative, part of HSC/E's contribution to the healthy workplace setting of Our Healthier Nation. This three-year strategy was launched by Tessa Jowell (Minister with responsibility for public health in England) and Alan Meale (Minister with responsibility for health and safety) in March 1999 and sets out to put health, including health and safety, into the mainstream of business life. The first 'strand' of the strategy was an initiative to tackle back pain which was launched in May 1999.

1.11   To signal our joint approach and to promote shared aims, the HSC signed a joint Statement of Intent with DOH. We are working to extend such collaboration to other public and private stakeholders, particularly small and medium-size businesses.

Developing a long-term occupational health strategy

1.12   HSC/E needs to consider what more needs to be done to reduce the current large toll of work-related ill health, while at the same time planning for a future world of work, by considering what occupational health problems might need to be tackled. The development of a forward strategy for occupational health for Great Britain involves consultation with, and the commitment of, a wide range of stakeholders. A new strategy provides an opportunity for all interested stakeholders to work in partnership to tackle the more difficult occupational health issues.

1.13   An HSE discussion document was published in August 1998 to widen the debate on the important issues that needed to be considered. Over 560 written responses were received. Other valuable comments on the discussion document were made at five open meetings and 40 conferences and workshops around the country. HSE is now considering the responses so that HSC can consider recommendations for a new strategy later in 1999. The new strategy will complement other government initiatives such as the Public Health strategies for England, Scotland and Wales.

Action in 1998/99

1.14   Work was undertaken to address occupational health issues across all sectors through a range of regulatory contacts and other activities, including:

- a draft consultative document and draft ACOP on **smoking at work**, which were circulated to key stakeholders in preparation for full consultation in 1999;

- a free leaflet on **work-related stress**, mainly targeted at small and medium-size firms and launched in September by Alan Meale. It received the Plain English Campaign's Clear English Standard and has become one of HSE's most requested publications, with around 59 000 copies issued so far;

- a working group set up by HSC's Occupational Health Advisory Committee to consider the feasibility of an ACOP on **stress**; a discussion document was published in April 1999;

- a major project to evaluate a petro-chemical company's arrangements for dealing with work-related **stress** was completed and a report is currently being prepared;

- consultation on whether guidance for employers on **post-incident trauma** is needed. The majority of those consulted were in favour of free guidance for employers;

- continued work through the Deep Mined Coal Industry Advisory Committee to secure improvements in health risk management, including a seminar on the management of health risks; focus on the use of solvents; work to promote awareness of hand-arm vibration syndrome in small **mines**; and continued research on diesel engine exhaust emissions underground leading to the identification of a new measurement technique;

- revised guidance on **radiation** *Keep your top on*, published in July 1998;

- revised guidance on **noise** *Ear protection, employers duties explained*, together with a pocket card *Protect your hearing!* and a poster published in October 1999;

- development of guidance on **musculoskeletal risks** in the chemicals industry, which will be published in April 2000;

- consultation on an ACOP to support the regulations to improve the provision of **first aid offshore;**

- the checking of safety arrangements for limiting occupational exposure to **radiation** at all 41 nuclear sites; an annual review of arrangements was also carried out with each site operator;

- 259 visits to workplaces where **legionella** is a potential hazard. Formal enforcement action was taken at 25-30% of all visits, including nine proposed prosecutions; and 103 visits to water treatment companies.

- a programme of visits to investigate **legionella** risks in the chemical manufacturing sector, leading to one successful prosecution;

- an inspection project on the management of **food hygiene risks** offshore, which showed that in general the management of food hygeine is very good - extensive work to improve standards was required in only one of 31 inspections; and

- initiatives by local authorities to raise awareness of **dermatitis** in hairdressers.

Occupational health support

1.15   Ministers have been concerned that lack of access to occupational health support contributes to health inequalities in the working population. At the end of 1997 Ministers invited HSC to undertake a programme of work, in liaison with the Department of Health (DOH), to advise the Government on ways of driving forward a framework of occupational health support aimed at improving access for everyone, especially those who work in small and medium-size enterprises (SMEs).

1.16   HSC's Occupational Health Advisory Committee (OHAC) set up a Working Group to develop advice for Ministers. The Working Group's recommendations were adopted by the main committee in March and were submitted via the Commission to Ministers in summer 1999. HSE also held a joint conference 'Towards Occupational Health Solution' with DOH in July 1998 to discuss ways of providing occupational health support to SMEs. The views expressed helped to inform the development of OHAC's advice.

Key priority for 1998/99: To improve health and safety at work by promoting the full participation of principal stake holders - employers, employees and their representatives - and key intermediaries

Working together more effectively

1.17   We already do a good deal to engage with others - we work closely with local authorities, employers and their organisations, trade unions and a wide range of intermediaries. We also have extensive consultative arrangements and advisory committees. Intermediaries, such as trade and professional associations, the major health and safety charities, consultancies and training organisations, have traditionally played an important part in the health and safety system. Their role has included providing advice to duty holders, including advice on the law and interpretation of the law and on HSE guidance, especially to small firms. But if we are to improve health and safety in a practical way we need to work with others more actively and positively. Structural changes in industry and changing patterns of employment, particularly the growth in SMEs, mean that we cannot act alone.

1.18   In 1997 we began a project to examine the current and potential role of key intermediaries. This included a questionnaire to and interviews with a number of key organisations. The main conclusion was that our stakeholders do not always have an entirely clear view of the priorities which are set out in HSC's Strategic Plan; and that there is scope to get those involved in the health and safety system to work more closely with us in achieving our objectives. This has led to important changes in the way we prepare and develop our plan. We will for instance be encouraging stakeholders to participate in the development and implementation of future plans and actively discussing with them what our collective strategy should be to improve standards of health and safety. As a first step in this process we held a major conference with stakeholders in May 1999.

1.19   An example of the valuable work which stakeholders carry out is the guide on *Safety and contractor/client relationships. The good practice guide for manufacturing* prepared during the year by the Engineering and Employers' Federation (EEF)/ HSE Contractor and Supplier Forum, which includes representatives from the UK's leading engineering manufacturing companies. The Guide was published by the EEF in July 1999.

1.20   The Commission's Industry and Advisory Committees are a key element of our work with others. They encourage the joint participation of all representatives in the improvement of health and safety at work. More information about their work can be found in Annex 5. Health and Safety Commissioners and members of the IACs attended a conference in December to discuss developments which might impact on the work of the IACs.

1.21   Other work across the organisation included:

- **HSE's Field Operations Directorate** (FOD) completed the first year of a pilot strategy to support the development of effective working relationships with key intermediaries such as Training and Enterprise

Councils (TECs) in order to reach small firms and business start-ups. The project established a baseline, including a survey of relationships between local HSE staff and their counterparts in intermediary organisations. This showed a mutual lack of understanding about roles and functions. A programme of contacts has now begun in Norfolk and London to exchange information about working methods and ways in which we can support each other;

- FOD inspectors and Workplace Contact Officers have been active with various local **occupational health and safety groups** across the country. These groups have a growing proportion of consultants and training providers who in turn influence small firms;

- the **Railway Inspectorate** (RI) continued to hold regular meetings with the main sources of influence within the railway industry. A new protocol has led to the introduction of quarterly meetings with Railtrack's senior management and to six-monthly meetings with Railtrack's zone directors. Following initial meetings with the main railway trade unions, it was agreed to hold regular regional meetings between inspectors and trade union officials. Three meetings of the European Chief Inspectors of Railways were held during the year to exchange information on enforcement problems and best practice;

- development of a **benchmarking** service for users of the *Health and safety climate survey tool*. This will enable data supplied by users of the tool to be maintained by a contractor for use by participating organisations for benchmarking purposes;

- a series of focus groups with duty holders under the **Construction** (Design and Management) Regulations (CDM) aimed at identifying difficulties with the Regulations and examples of good practice. Particular effort was made to involve smaller companies and safety representatives. As a result the Health and Safety Commission has decided to revise the ACOP in order to improve understanding of and compliance with the CDM;

- the **Directorate of Science and Technology** continued to work with professional bodies and institutions to recognise the principles of risk management and inherently safer design as mandatory parts of degree courses and professional accreditation. They have also started work on a project to look at childrens' ability to assess and manage risks, using a secondee from education;

- a short **video** *Escaping the maze* and booklet, to help people find answers to health and safety questions, including information services available from intermediaries;

- publication of revised guidance and a workers' leaflet on safety representatives and safety committees **offshore** in May 1998;

- HSC's Oil Industry Advisory Committee has identified the need to work with stakeholders to develop a strategic agenda for the next five to ten years. New work has begun to identify current health and safety initiatives and this will inform further work with key players to take forward a strategy for 1999/2000; and

- HSE's **Chemical and Hazardous Installations Division** (CHID) established the Chemicals Industry Forum (CIF) in 1998, as the main means of involving principal stakeholders in their work. The CIF meets three times a year.

Local authorities

1.22   Our partnership with local authorities is a vital part of fulfilling our statutory functions and making an impact in local communities. They have a key role to play as intermediaries themselves and are well placed to help other intermediaries. The Local Authority Unit and the Health and Safety Executive / Local Authorities Enforcement Liaison committee (HELA) have already developed an effective dialogue with key stakeholders from business through regular meetings of the HELA Dialogue with Business. HELA have also set up similar meetings with trade unions, the first of which was held in December 1998.

1.23   As part of HELA's strategy to develop and enhance the role of intermediaries in the local authority enforced sector, an award for innovative projects was made at its annual conference in November. Projects recognised included work on health and safety training, and advice and guidance for business in collaboration with local colleges and training centres, Business Links, TECs and trade associations.

1.24   More detailed information about the work of local authorities can be found in the *HELA annual report 1999: Health and safety in the local authority enforced sectors,* published in July 1999.

Employee representatives

1.25   The participation of employees and their representatives in matters relating to their health and safety is vital in improving health and safety standards in the workplace. Research suggests that organisations which involve their employees, particularly trade union safety representatives, have a significantly better health and safety record. However there has been a decline in the number of workplaces with recognised trade unions, and the Health and Safety (Consultation with Employees) Regulations 1996 have only had a limited impact in non-unionised workplaces. We need to find ways to reach smaller organisations who may not have access to advice and guidance from health and safety professionals. A broad programme of action is underway to look for effective ways to promote employee participation and increase its effectiveness:

- We carried out a review of the contacts that inspectors make with safety representatives and employees during routine inspections. This has enabled us to identify further action we can take to develop this, including revision of guidance to inspectors and a FOD **Quality and Improvement Programme** for contact with safety representatives.

- In March the Commission agreed plans to **review consultation arrangements**; research began in January to inform this review and assess the effectiveness of current regulations on consultation. A report will be issued in autumn 1999.

- HSE is directly promoting the work of safety representatives, for instance through **safety representatives' conferences** - the first of these was held in November 1998. Future events are planned to coincide with the consultation period when we issue our discussion document in autumn 1999.

- CHID and CIF have agreed to a research project to find examples of good practice in **workforce involvement.** Work will commence during 1999/2000.

- A revised leaflet for workers about the regulations governing the role and functions of safety representatives and safety committees on **offshore** installations was published in January 1999.

- During routine contact with duty holders in the railways industry, inspectors encouraged larger railway companies to provide help and advice to their smaller companies, including very small contractors.

Bringing poor practice to light

1.26   HSE and local authorities have procedures in place that enable employees and others to raise concerns about circumstances where they think their employer is exposing them to risks or is not carrying out their legal duties. Complainants are not identified to the employer unless they have said they do not object to this. We receive over 20 000 complaints a year and respond in accordance with HSC's policy on enforcement.

1.27   Our Field Operations Directorate (FOD) developed **new procedures for handling complaints**, to enable them to make the most appropriate response and to ensure the best use of resources. The new procedures came into effect at the end of 1998/99 and we expect to see the benefits during 1999/2000.

1.28   In addition FOD ran two **pilot trials** to progress an initiative to bring poor health and safety practice to light. The pilots were designed to:

- help assess the value and impact of enhanced publicity for HSE's arrangements for handling complaints about employers;

- test current procedures in FOD for handling complaints; and

- help evaluate how useful complaints of this kind are in bringing poor practice to light.

1.29   The trials were held over a four month period. Local press advertisements were run in both areas throughout the campaign, supplemented by local radio advertising and advertisements on local transport. A dedicated 'Worksafe' telephone number was given in the advertisements. The pilots showed that :

- the publicity resulted in 203 additional calls, of which 56 were complaints, representing an increase of 6.3% on complaints received through normal channels;

- the complaints handling system which introduced new procedures in HSE is a success. Standards of information taken from callers, clear-up rate and speed of response have all improved; and

- targeted initiatives of this kind have an important part to play in ensuring that employees are aware of who to contact about health and safety concerns, and are more likely to be effective than wide-ranging schemes.

1.30   The Commission's view is that where it is possible to resolve concerns about an organisation's health and safety arrangements internally, this is generally the most effective way. In 1998/99 we funded a study by Public Concern at Work to examine the value of internal reporting systems which enable employees to report concerns and to consider the barriers which prevent employees from doing so. The findings are contained in *Safety cultures; Giving staff a clear role*, published in April 1999. We are currently considering the need for guidance for employers based on this research.

Key priority for 1998/99: To cut injury rates, particularly in the agriculture, construction and manufacturing sectors, especially by influencing duty holders through regulatory contacts, including preventive inspection

Responding to injury rates

1.31   Ultimately all of our work is about reducing injuries and ill health arising from work activities. Injuries at work kill around 300 people every year and although fatal injuries are at an historically low level, the results for 1996/97 showed that there was still room for further improvement. We were particularly concerned and disappointed at the rise in fatalities in the agriculture, construction and manufacturing sectors, and we carried out major programmes of work within these sectors to help bring about a reduction in injury rates.

1.32   Estimated final figures indicate that there were 257 fatal injuries to workers (employees and self-employed) in 1998/99, compared to 274 in 1997/98. These figures look like being one of the lowest on record since the introduction of the Reporting of Injuries, Disease and Dangerous Occurrences Regulations (RIDDOR). The number of fatal injuries to workers fell in the construction, extractive and service industries. However, the number of fatalities to the self-employed increased in agriculture and the number of fatalities to employees increased in manufacturing. See Part Two of this Report for more detailed information about health and safety statistics.

Agriculture

Table 1 Self-employed in the agriculture sector: fatal injuries and fatal injury rate (rates per 100 000 in brackets).

1993/94	1994/95	1995/96	1996/97	1997/98	1998/99 (ef)*
22 (9.9)	32 (12.9)	20 (8.3)	35 (14.3)	20 (8.7)	30 (15.0)

* *ef: estimated final.*

1.33   The number of fatal injuries to the **self-employed** each year in agriculture has fluctuated considerably since 1991/92. Estimated final figures indicate that there were 30 fatalities in 1998/99, compared with 20 in 1997/98 and 35 in 1996/97. The injury rate for the self-employed is expected to be 15.0 per 100 000 in 1998/99, the highest level since 1991/92. A fall in the number of self-employed people in the sector in 1998/99 also contributed to the increase in the rate.

1.34   HSE cannot rely solely on preventive inspection and other regulatory contacts to reach people in this sector. Our approach is to improve safety management in the industry and to reinforce positive attitudes towards safety in the workforce. This means continuing our work in partnership with local authorities and with stakeholders such as the Transport and General Workers Union and the National Farmers Union, and using a range of other contact methods such as guidance, publicity and education.

1.35   In 1998/99 we carried out a broad programme of work, including:

- **regional inspection blitzes**: the national initiative involved 111 inspectors and 3855 inspection visits, during a series of two-week inspection blitzes to farms and forestry operations, targeting mainly transport, child safety and forestry work - these resulted in 723 enforcement notices and 14 prosecution cases; the blitzes showed that in the forestry industry, although the essential elements of safe working practices are known, the control of contractors by those higher up the chain is particularly poor. Despite enhanced local publicity in which farmers were encouraged to look at their working practices and check machinery, nearly one in five premises had standards that warranted enforcement;

- revision of the **Prevention of Accidents to Children Regulations** and supporting ACOP, aimed at reducing the number of accidents to children in agriculture; and a national publicity campaign, supported by preventive inspections and other regulatory activity, to reduce the number of **children** killed and injured in agriculture from the ten year average of 5 per annum. Child safety was discussed at each farm visit and a copy of the leaflet *Accidents to children* was issued. Thousands of children and teachers were contacted through events such as open nights and days, special child safety presentations and also by inspectors using child safety as a major theme at shows and demonstrations. The campaign resulted in 121 improvement notices, one prohibition notice and 11 prosecutions. Provisional statistics for 1998/99 indicate that three children were killed as a result of agricultural work, one of the lowest figures ever;

- national and regional seminars and visits to the head offices of 14 national companies to improve health and safety management of those using **contractors in the forestry industry**. This initiative has changed the way health and safety is managed in forestry and raised awareness, particularly amongst forest owners. It has resulted in the development of a management framework for health and safety in commercial forestry and woodland operations which has been favourably received within the industry. This initiative will continue in 1999/00;

- the first part of a three-year programme aimed at **reducing the number of transport-related fatal and major injuries** by at least 10% over the next three years. This work linked in with a national publicity campaign. The 503 contacts made were targeted at specific hazards in agriculture and wood-working premises. Formal enforcement action was taken at 20% of visits. Some areas carried out 'transport blitzes', involving local police spot checks of vehicles. A video *Fatal traction* and a free leaflet on transport risks were produced;

- five seminars for **manufacturers, importers and suppliers of agricultural machines** and over 70 individual follow up visits. The agricultural sector also attended 14 meetings of CEN European standards committees to negotiate the maintenance of high standards of health and safety;

- continued work with agricultural colleges to enhance **health and safety education in the curriculum**; the agriculture and wood sector continued to produce lecturers' training packs and videos targeted specifically at young people entering the industry. Some colleges have amended their syllabuses to incorporate health and safety in the curricula and in particular to use the lecturer training packs;

16

- work to raise the profile of health and safety through **agricultural shows, demonstrations and seminars** - including three major advertising campaigns on transport, forestry and children; a press launch of the transport video *Tractor action*; the forestry initiative on the *Management of health and safety in forestry;* publication of the *Fatal injuries report; Farmwise,* a new comprehensive guide to health and safety in agriculture, which will be sent free to all farmers in Great Britain; attendance at around 60 agricultural shows; two pilot health roadshows focusing mainly on musculoskeletal and respiratory disorders; and 20 seminars on the new framework for health and safety in forestry;

- work to improve **communication between HSC/E and stakeholders** in the agricultural sector, including evening meetings of the HSC Chairman and employer/employee representatives of the farming community (see paragraph 1.47);

- work to raise the profile of health and safety with **other government departments**, for example the Ministry of Agriculture, Fisheries and Food's (MAFF) work on gangmasters; FOD took part in two 'operation gangmaster' events, involving seven other government departments. The events provided useful intelligence and information to enable HSE to better target its inspections; and

- work to raise awareness of health issues including **zoonoses, safe uses of pesticides and musculoskeletal problems**; issues such as the revised MAFF/HSE Code of Practice on the *Safe use of pesticides* and the implementation of Integrated Crop Management were raised during 270 farm visits; the *Pesticides incidents report for 1997/98* was published during the year.

Construction

Table 2 Workers in the construction sector: fatal injuries and fatal injury rate (rates per one hundred thousand in brackets)

1993/94	1994/95	1995/96	1996/97	1997/98	1998/99(ef)*
91 (5.7)	83 (5.1)	79 (5.0)	90 (5.6)	80 (4.6)	66 (3.8)

* *ef: estimated final.*

1.36   The number of fatal injuries to **workers** in construction is expected to fall by 18% in 1998/99, compared with the previous year. The final fatal injury rate is expected to fall from 4.6 to 3.8 per 100 000 workers, the lowest level since 1991/92.

1.37   With the introduction of the CDM and the Construction (Health, Safety and Welfare) Regulations 1996 (CHSW) we now have in place a robust legislative framework for the construction industry. Our major efforts have been directed at ensuring this legislation is embedded in the culture of the industry. Current health and safety performance will be greatly improved if structured and effective health and safety management is applied consistently across the industry. The existing legislative framework establishes the basis for this and recognises that all the key players of the industry - clients, designers, contractors and the workforce have a part to play in improving the industry. Industry has responded positively and the last few years have been characterised by a greater willingness for industry and regulators to share initiatives and take things forward jointly. This has been helpful as an isolated HSE approach cannot be as effective as co-operative working.

1.38   Where possible we are forging links with stakeholders, for example the Chief Inspector of Construction is now a member of the Construction Industry Board and also a member of the Government Construction Client Panel (a committee led by HM Treasury which brings together government departments in order to establish good practice as construction clients). These offer an excellent opportunity to spread our health and safety messages.

1.39   During the year we carried out a major programme of work, including:

- a concentrated **inspection campaign** targeting those who flout the law; this included 100 visits during one week to scaffolding sites in Westminster - inspectors had to stop virtually all scaffolding and 50 prohibition notices were served where standards could not be put right; the campaign received widespread publicity and will continue into 1999/00; an intensive inspection blitz of Glasgow city centre scaffolding, involving visits to 82 sites and resulting in 12 prohibition notices; in the North West region large city centres were subject to an inspection blitz concentrating on roof work, public protection, falls from heights and refurbishment jobs - 262 contacts were made and over 60 enforcement notices served;

- the start of a two year programme aimed at eliminating all **falls through fragile roof lights** by 2000/01, by targeting specification of roof light materials; over a thousand contacts were made to 'new' duty holders which showed that the majority of roof light installations seen or planned were non-fragile. This positive result was probably due to considerable pre-campaign publicity which involved notifying all relevant trade and professional organisations and manufacturers/suppliers. There were some reports of efforts to 'design out' roof lights altogether. The campaign will continue during 1999/00;

- publication of revised guidance *Health and safety in roofwork*, launched in November 1998 by the Chief Inspector of Construction; and

- new guidance on **construction site transport** *The safe use of vehicles on construction*, launched in December 1998 at the Millennium Dome site in Greenwich; the guidance represents part of the wider HSE transport initiative.

1.40   Other work to secure real improvements in health and safety standards in the construction industry included focus group meetings with duty holders under the CDM. Twelve meetings were held last year. We have taken away a number of important messages from the focus groups and we are taking measures to address them. These include:

- encouraging local authorities to incorporate information about client duties under the CDM in the local authority operated planning process;

- developing a leaflet about client duties for designers to give to clients; and

- revision of the ACOP *Managing construction for health and safety*, to clarify requirements under the CDM.

1.41   The European Commission is developing a directive on temporary work equipment at heights. This will have an influence not only in the construction industry but also for other major users of work equipment at heights, particularly in agriculture and manufacturing. We are in the process of establishing an internal and external advisory group to work on this.

Manufacturing

Table 3 Employees in the manufacturing sector: fatal injuries and fatal injury rate (rates per one hundred thousand in brackets)

1993/94	1994/95	1995/96	1996/97	1997/98	1998/99 (ef)*
59 (1.6)	46 (1.2)	42 (1.1)	53(1.3)	54 (1.3)	65 (1.6)

* ef: estimated final.

1.42   Estimated final figures indicate that the number of fatal injuries to **employees** in manufacturing increased by 20% in 1998/99 compared with the previous year. The fatal injury rate for employees increased from 1.3 to 1.6 per 100 000. Ten more workers died than in 1997/98, 71 compared to 61. The most noticeable increases in the number of fatalities have been in the manufacture of basic metals and fabricated metal products - where deaths have risen from 14 in 1997/98 to 24 in 1998/99. In contrast, the major injury rate for workers is expected to fall by 6%, to 192 per 100 000, compared to 205 in 1997/98.

1.43   In addition to routine inspection visits in the manufacturing sector, FOD undertook specific action in manufacturing to improve the management of health and safety in premises where injury rates were the highest in their sector, including paper mills, food factories and engineering premises. Action in 1998/99 included:

- **visits to all paper mills:** in 1997/98 the injury incidence rate in the paper making industry was three times that of the manufacturing industry for over-3-day injuries and more than twice that for major injuries. During the year the programme to improve the management of health and safety at the 12 poorest performing paper mills was extended to include all paper mills. Each mill produced prioritised action plans to improve their management performance; a common feature of poor performance was found to be a low level of employee participation in health and safety;

- **visits to food factories:** the food and drink industry has the highest reported injury incidence rate of any manufacturing sector and twice that of the average in manufacturing generally. Managers of poor performing sites attended a sector run seminar on practical ways of managing health and safety. During the year inspectors visited 16 large premises which reported a disproportionate number of injuries. Around half were found to comply with the key requirements of good health and safety management; and figures show a reduction in injury rate of 50% for two of the sites; and

- **visits to engineering premises**: in the engineering sector, inspectors targeted 63 engineering premises with high injury incidence rates, during which they promoted the sector's health and safety guidance. Health and safety action plans have been put in place as a result of the visits.

Key priority for 1998/99: To take forward HSC'S strategy for reaching small firms

1.44   We are committed to ensuring that the health and safety system leads to improvements in health and safety performance in small firms. Statistical data analysed for the years 1994/95 and 1995/96 indicate that the risk of fatal and of amputation injury in small manufacturing workplaces (fewer than 50 employees) is double that of larger workplaces (more than 200 employees). Injuries and ill health are neither acceptable nor inevitable and improving health and safety in small firms will remain a priority.

1.45   The needs of small firms are now firmly embedded in much of what we do. For example, they are very much the primary focus for the Good Health is Good Business campaign. In working to improve health and safety in small firms our aim is to consult directly with them whenever and wherever possible; to provide advice, information and guidance which is appropriate to their needs; and to work with key intermediary organisations in communicating important health and safety messages.

1.46   We continued our work through the **Good Neighbour scheme,** which recognises the impact larger firms, in their relationships with contractors, suppliers, neighbouring businesses, etc, can have on improving health and safety standards in small firms. The scheme was a major theme of the European Week for Safety and Health (19-25 October 1998). Key intermediaries, including major trades unions, were encouraged to support the Week . There was an excellent response - the best ever. Over 10 000 action packs were distributed and nearly 2000 questionnaires were returned.

1.47   The Commission continued to attend **breakfast meeting and evening seminars with small firms** to hear their views first hand. In 1998/99 these included two breakfast meetings with local authority environmental health officers and two evening meetings with the agriculture sector. The breakfast meetings, held in Brighton (November 1998) and Norwich (May 1999), both attracted around 100 delegates and gave small businesses the opportunity to meet and question health and safety policy makers and enforcers on a wide range of issues of interest to small firms. Similarly, the success of the two agriculture sector meetings held in Clynderwen, West Wales (October 1998) and Darlington, North East Yorkshire (March 1999) emphasised the benefits of face-to-face events as a means for improving communication and getting important health and safety messages across.

1.48   **Good Neighbour Forums** have been set up to encourage supportive relationships between large firms and small contractors, suppliers and neighbouring firms who can readily be influenced by the policies and actions of the large firms with whom they do business:

*   The first **Good Neighbour forum** was launched by the Health and Safety Minister Alan Meale during the European Week for Safety and Health in Newcastle upon Tyne. The event was organised in partnership with UNISON, and participating organisations were the three largest employers in the region, Newcastle upon Tyne City Council, Northern Electric and Northumbrian Water.

*   Each of the major organisations invited their safety committee members and a selection of small contracting firms and suppliers. Others have been held in Manchester, in partnership with the Trafford

Park Business Forum, and in the East Midlands, with the Engineering Employers Federation (EEF) and its East Midlands Association.

1.49   As part of the Good Neighbour scheme we contacted over 800 training organisations to invite them to promote health and safety. A large number responded with some offering free training courses and training needs analysis to small businesses. We also worked with the British Safety Council, ROSPA and the EEF to stimulate good practice through the promotion of the scheme in their health and safety management awards.

1.50   Other initiatives to reach small firms through a wide range of intermediaries continued throughout the year. Of particular importance was the establishment of a **Smaller Companies Forum** by the EEF to improve dialogue with small firms. Membership of the forum is drawn from a wide range of business and professional organisations. The first meeting took place in November 1998.

1.51   Other action across the organisation included:

- a new **pilot strategy by FOD** for improving relationships with business support organisations, in order to improve channels for getting health and safety information to small firms (see paragraph 1.21 for more detail):

- Open Days and ten workshops run by the **Electrical Equipment Certification Service** (EECS), to give small firms advice on what they need to do to comply with health and safety law on the manufacture, use, installation and repair of equipment in explosive atmospheres;

- over 200 visits to **diving contractors** to give advice on the new diving regulations; assistance to local authorities in the investigation of recreational diving accidents including presentations at local authority seminars; and production of a video *Dive shop inspection* for local authority inspectors;

- HSE's **Chemicals Industries Forum** (CIF) reviewed occupational health issues within small and medium sized firms (SMEs) in the chemical industry and a working group was set up to review occupational health data collected by the industry; a working group has been set up to focus initially on the reduction of musculoskeletal disorders and will develop guidance and a long-term programme of initiatives;

- a local initiative to improve the level of compliance with the CHIP Regulations within SMEs in the **chemicals** industry, which included breakfast seminars, questionnaires and an enforcement programme. This initiative will continue into 1999/00;

- CIF was extended to include representation from the **explosives** industry and subsequently a new contact group for SMEs was formed for companies involved in the supply and use of explosives in the offshore oil exploration and production industry;

- a one-year national publicity campaign on **workplace transport safety** and the first year of a three-year FOD inspection programme (aimed at reducing the number of transport-related fatal and major injuries by at least 10% over the next three years), in partnership with some local authorities; this included visits to agricultural/forestry/wood working premises, quarries and construction sites -

over 2000 contacts were made resulting in over 80 improvement notices and 35 prohibition notices; and

- the Local Authority Unit produced video training packages for **local authorities** on consistency of enforcement in builders merchants and the tyre and exhaust industry.

Action by HSE and local authorities to help small firms

1.52   As part of the Health and Safety Executive/ Local Authorities Enforcement Liaison Committee's (HELA) Small Firms Strategy, HELA produced a **Good Practice Pack** *Delivering the goods - an enforcement good practice pack for local authorities,* which disseminates information on local authority initiatives to help small firms comply with health and safety law. Initiatives based on examples of good practice in the pack, including novel approaches to low risk SMEs using mailshots, partnerships with business, consultancy and self-help schemes, are being developed and piloted by local authorities in three counties. For example:

- some local authorities have developed self-assessment packages in the form of a questionnaire and sent them to low risk premises which would not normally be inspected. Those who do not return the questionnaire will be inspected and 10% of the subject group will be visited to inform the evaluation of the pilot; and

- another group of local authorities is attempting to improve RIDDOR reporting by mailing information and questionnaires to small businesses, with follow up visits and further advice.

1.53   The **Lead Authority Partnership Scheme**, which was set up to improve consistency in approaches to large national companies and provide a liaison point on key issues has continued to develop. The scheme has now been extended to include more flexible arrangements by which smaller companies, trade associations and their members can benefit from a link with a lead authority. Fifteen **pilot partnerships** have been set up to test these arrangements and are being independently evaluated. Ten are between local authorities and individual companies; two involve trade associations; and three are solely concerned with petroleum issues. The partnerships are more flexible than by a strict protocol.

Regulatory contacts

1.54   In addition to these initiatives we continued our important work to help small firms through regulatory contacts such as preventive inspections and investigations. Many small firms were targeted during specific inspection initiatives, including blitzes in the agriculture and construction industry (see paragraphs 135 to 139). **In 1998/99 79% of planned inspections carried out by HSE's Field Operations Directorate (FOD) were to small firms.**

1.55   Other forms of contact included extensive mailshots, including to 600 agricultural premises, around 130 engineering intermediaries, roof workers and plant hire companies; and a wide range of seminars including for forestry contractors, duty holders in the construction industry and for builders on gas safety requirements.

1.56   We continued to work, through inspectors and workplace contact officers (WCOs), to identify new and unregistered premises and to make initial contact within two months of hearing about them. In the Home Counties region WCOs carried out joint sweeps of industrial estates with Environmental Health Officers to compare registration lists, agree enforcement allocation and identify higher risk premises which justified immediate inspection. See also Section 2 of this report which sets out our efforts to secure compliance with the law in line with the principles of proportionality, consistency, transparency and targeting, and our work to provide appropriate information and advice.

New guidance for small firms

- *Managing risk - adding value : How big firms manage contractual relations to reduce risk,* published in April 1998; and *Working together - Guidance on health and safety for contractors and suppliers,* also published in April 1998.

- *5 steps to risk assessment,* aimed at small firms, was redesigned and relaunched in May 1998; and further guidance *5 steps to risk assessment: case studies* was published in September 1998.

- *COSHH essentials,* guidance for SMEs on the control of health risks from **chemicals**, was published in May 1999.

- Simple guidance for small firms on the **Provision and Use of Work Equipment Regulations,** and the **Lifting Operations and Lifting Equipment Regulations** was published in April 1999.

- An **electronically supported version of *Essentials of health and safety at work*** has been developed in co-operation with Royal Sun Alliance. It was demonstrated at the Safety and Health at Work Exhibition at Earls Court in March 1999, and is expected to be launched in the autumn. This will enable small businesses to do a health and safety review and prepare a risk assessment and safety policy.

Evaluation and research

1.57   HSC's training initiative included research into the level and quality of health and safety training undertaken by businesses, including small firms. This small scale study involved 500 telephone interviews, broadly split between employee representatives and seniors (ie. the person with overall responsibility for health and safety). The study revealed that three in four employee representatives and two in three seniors received either internal or external health and safety training. A significant number received no health and safety training. The findings suggested that larger sites had a more formal structure for the provision of health and safety training.

1.58   Work is underway to evaluate the passport training scheme for contractors, which is operated by the Client/Contractor National Safety Group (CCNSG). The scheme involves the provision of health and safety awareness training to contractors' employees. Trainees are tested on their knowledge before obtaining a 'passport' to work on the sites of clients who participate in the CCNSG scheme. The scheme is administered by the Engineering Construction Industry Training Board and widely used by the chemical manufacturing sector and utilities. The work is complete and and the report will be published in 1999/2000.

1.59   A research report *Evaluating the impact of contact techniques* which looks at the effectiveness of mailshots and seminars in persuading employers to improve their standards of health and safety, showed that both techniques were effective in stimulating change, though mailshots to a lesser degree. This research forms part of HSE's aim to reach and communicate with more small firms - an important challenge since firms employing fewer than 50 people represent 97% of all businesses in this country.

1.60   Research on the *Introduction to health and safety* booklet was carried out, showing a high degree of recall and increased awareness of health and safety following its publication. A high percentage stated it was the first time they had seen any health and safety information and a high number also claimed to have taken action as a result.

Regulations to prevent major accident hazards

1.61   The new Control of Major Accident Hazards Regulations 1999 (COMAH) came into force on 1 April 1999, to implement the Seveso II Directive.

1.62   The new Regulations aim to prevent major chemical accidents which could harm both people and the environment and we have been working closely with the Department of the Environment Transport and the Regions and the environment agencies to ensure that both elements are sufficiently covered. The Regulations will apply at sites with significant quantities of dangerous substances including major companies in the chemical industry, which is one of the UK's largest manufacturing industries.

A new competent authority

1.63   COMAH will be enforced by a new competent authority which comprises HSE, the Environment Agency in England and Wales and the Scottish Environment Protection Agency. This has meant a major enterprise in joined up government to develop the procedures and systems to ensure a consistent approach to the assessment of safety reports and the management of the assessment process. To ensure the continued effective working between HSE and the environment agencies we have drawn up **memoranda of understanding,** under which constituent parts of the competent authority will work together to carry out their enforcement functions and ensure the industry is properly regulated with the minimum of duplication.

Important new duty on HSE as the regulator

1.64   Although the Regulations will impose some new obligations on operators, they also place an entirely new and explicit duty on HSE as the regulator to assess operators' safety reports. The safety report requires operators to demonstrate that they have met the requirements of the Regulations and in particular that major accident hazards are under control.

1.65   HSE and the environment agencies, as regulators working in partnership, will be required to assess both the technical and managerial elements contained in each safety report with a timebound obligation to inform operators of the outcome of our analysis. This has added importance because, if assessment of the safety report and subsequent site inspection reveals a serious deficiency in the employer's arrangements for preventing and mitigating major accidents, the installation will be prohibited from operating.

New guidance - assessment principles and acceptance criteria

1.66   Safety report assessment principles and procedures were completed, including assessment criteria for the evaluation of safety reports, in consultation with the environment agencies and other key stakeholders. These were piloted in four companies. Following comments from industry representatives we have published **guidance** based on these assessment criteria, but aimed at those responsible for preparing the safety reports. We also published a **leaflet** aimed at those who may be affected by major hazard sites, such as workers, representatives and local residents. An **assessment manual** which describes the principles, procedures and criteria for assessment was prepared ahead of the Regulations coming into force and is available to all inspectors in the competent authority. This has enabled the training of over 240 inspectors to go ahead at an early stage. A copy of the manual has been placed on HSE's website.

1.67   We have developed the guidance and procedures in an open way to enable all those with an interest in COMAH to understand the arrangements under which the competent authority will operate and the measures which operators will need to take to ensure compliance.

1.68   We are also developing **electronically-based guidance for inspectors** on assessing technical aspects of safety reports . This will be available only in electronic format and will be placed on HSE's Intranet. In 1999/00 discussions will be held with industry with a view to extending the guidance to include internal standards from individual companies. This will help to ensure consistency in the enforcement of standards by inspectors.

Multi-site employers

1.69   As part of our safety report assessment and inspection strategies we are developing arrangements for dealing with multi-site employers in the most effective and efficient way. This is particularly relevant for COMAH where the work of the competent authority will be charged directly to the operator. (See Section 3, paragraphs 1.92 to 1.93 for details of work on charging.) For large organisations we are identifying a Lead Unit to co-ordinate contacts with the employer and to agree arrangements for the handling of safety reports.

Major work in 1998/99

During the year we have worked closely with our stakeholders in preparing for the successful introduction of COMAH. Key work completed includes:

*   publication of a **consultative document** in May 1998, containing proposals for regulations and guidance to implement the COMAH Directive;

*   setting in place robust systems and procedures to deal with assessment of **safety case reports**;

*   publication of **guidance** for industry on compliance with the new regulations;

*   preparation of an effective **inspection** programme for COMAH establishments; and

*   completion of the **recruitment programme** - 11 inspectors were recruited by December 1998 and another five will take up post in early 1999/00. Training continued throughout the year.

Section 2

How we performed against our continuing aims

> **Continuing aim 1: To modernise, simplify and support the regulatory framework, including European Union and other international work**

Resources 1998/99				
Aim 1	Staff years	% Staff years	Staff costs £k	% Staff costs
Planned	616	16.9	21 704	19.3
Outturn	617	17.4	21 717	20.0

1.70   We are responsible for developing policy and proposing legislation in response to new risks, government initiatives and implementing the requirements of European Union (EU) legislative instruments. We are committed to helping business - small firms in particular - by simplifying and clarifying health and safety law and guidance; improving the enforcement regime by ensuring it is consistent, proportionate, transparent and targeted; and cutting red tape by removing unnecessary forms and paperwork requirements.

Better and more effective regulation

1.71   The Commission concluded the programme of action to implement its 1994 Review of Regulation report. The programme represented a major step forward in action to remove unnecessary burdens on business by removing redundant legislation and improving the quality of guidance, particularly that targeted at small firms. New procedures have been introduced to quality control new guidance and ensure that it is targeted at the right audience.

1.72   There is a continuing commitment to respond to government initiatives on Regulatory Impact. This includes contributing to several Cabinet Office Regulatory Impact Unit and interdepartmental projects on 'one-stop-shopping' and electronic government.

1.73   Annex 2 gives details of legislative projects started, continuing or completed during 1998/99. They include:

- a package of regulations, ACoP and guidance for the **quarries industry**. This package will implement the Extractive Industries Directive in quarries and replace 12 pieces of existing quarries legislation - a significant removal of unnecessary, inappropriate, outdated and sometimes almost incomprehensible legislation;

- two sets of regulations, the Provision and Use of Work Equipment Regulations and the Lifting Operations and Lifting Equipment Regulations , implemented the Amending Directive to the **Use of Work Equipment** Directive. This was one of the largest legislative packages undertaken since the implementation of the Six-pack of Directives but despite it size and complexity was implemented on time;

- the consolidation of the various sets of **Gas Safety** (Installations and Use) Regulations into a single set was completed on schedule but the subsequent review planned for the registration/competence aspects has been radically extended into a fundamental review of the whole gas safety regime. The review will also pilot alternative consultation processes; and

- revised **Health and Safety (Enforcing Authority)** Regulations were introduced. These clarify the enforcing responsibilities of HSE and local authorities and reduce duplication and inconsistency.

1.74   The **Control of Substances Hazardous to Health** (COSHH) Regulations were amended in June 1998 and further consolidated in March 1999, introducing or updating occupational exposure limits for a number of chemical substances, and reforming the procedure for making future changes. Authority has now been granted to HSC to specify certain exposure limits which will allow future changes to exposure limits to be introduced without amendment and republishing of the Regulations.

1.75   The mining legislation review programme was significantly delayed because of difficulty in obtaining stakeholder agreement to an element of one regulatory package. Further work to obtain consensus agreement to the package will be undertaken in the coming year.

Environmental appraisal

1.76   In response to the Government's guidance on Policy Appraisal and the Environment, published in 1998, we reaffirmed our commitment to considering environmental implications in developing our policies, legislation and guidance at an early stage and reflecting them in Regulatory Impact Assessments. The guidance was widely circulated and publicised and a seminar was held to raise awareness of this and other policy appraisal initiatives. We also contributed to the Government's new document *A better quality of life - a strategy for the sustainable development for the UK,* published in May 1999.

Responding to changing patterns of employment

1.77   As part the Commission's programme of work on the health and safety implications of changing patterns of employment, a project looked at the application of the Health and Safety at Work etc Act 1974 to the self-employed. A key conclusion was that some employers misunderstood that those self-employed for tax purposes may still, in terms of health and safety at work law, be employees for whom they had significant legal duties. A standard form of words for inclusion when appropriate in HSC/E guidance was agreed.

Working in Europe

1.78   This year we took the lead for the UK Government in the negotiation of nine EC Directives (See Annex 3 for details). We were also responsible for taking forward the implementation of ten others including the Control of Major Accident Hazards (the COMAH Directive). Important ongoing work included the Biocidal Products Directive and the Basic Safety Standards Directive (Ionising Radiation).

1.79   HSE's Information Services act as the UK focal point of the European Agency for Safety and Health at Work. It works to ensure a co-ordinated response for the Agency on behalf of the UK, including the social partners, and making and improving links with Northern Ireland agencies and social partners.

UK Presidency of the European Union

1.80   In the second half of the Presidency we played a key role in assisting UK Ministers to influence the EU to develop new proposals to ban the importation and use of white asbestos and to strengthen standards of protection for workers exposed to asbestos. HSE acted as a catalyst in enabling the EC to organize a pioneering seminar for Chief Executives of all Member States' health and safety authorities. HSE hosted, in Edinburgh, the successful Third European Film and Multimedia Festival on health and safety, and organized a conference in Cardiff on the training of labour inspectors, which included participants from all Member States and those countries applying for EU membership. Both events helped to ensure that we were able to explain effectively to our counterparts elsewhere in the Community, approaches to health and safety in the UK.

Helping the EU applicant countries

1.81   We delivered 25 projects with the EU applicant countries to provide technical expertise on implementation and enforcement of EC law. The projects were wide-ranging and included the culmination of a three year programme to assist Poland in the implementation of EC legislation on the classification, packaging and labelling of dangerous substances; the hosting of a short study visit to the UK of Bulgarian officials to discuss the UK health and safety system and its operation in practice; and the provision of technical assistance to the European Bank for Reconstruction and Development for the assistance programme to the Ukraine.

International developments

1.82   With an international trade in chemicals, protecting people from risk requires international standards and better information on chemical risk. Global harmonisation work brings benefits for the sound management of chemicals and the protection of people. We contributed to the process of rationalising the different international chemical risk assessment systems and took the lead in the work to develop a harmonised system for classifying hazardous chemicals, agreed in September 1998. This is the foundation for further work to develop harmonised systems for classifying mixtures and for hazard communication.

1.83   We contributed to an international United Nations Working Party leading to the revision of the UN Manual Tests for allocation of hazard divisions in the classification of explosives.

1.84   We organised a conference 'Changing health and Safety offshore - the agenda for the next 10 years' aimed at bringing together international regulators and all those connected with the offshore oil and gas industry. Over 300 delegates attended, representing the offshore oil and gas industry, trade unions, the offshore workforce, regulators from other countries and academics.

Key outputs

1.85   The key outputs in the box below - numbers of regulations, Approved Codes of Practice, consultative documents and guidance documents introduced - reflect the formal policy products that are produced by HSE to improve and modernise the legal framework of health and safety law, including the issue of authoritative guidance on standards. We came in slightly under target with this measure (plan 70, outturn 66) mainly due to problems with accurately forecasting the number of products required, dealing with unplanned work, and other factors beyond HSE's control such as changes to the legislative timetable made by other government departments.

1.86   In reality the formal type of output is just one dimension of our policy work which also includes supporting expert health and safety committees, dealing with non-statutory standard making, operational policy work (eg interpreting standards for specific industries), and the provision of economic and statistical support for policy formulation - all of which are difficult to quantify in terms of conventional output or outcome measures. Work is proceeding in this area to try to design meaningful measures of performance, particularly outcome and quality indicators.

Key outputs and quality measures	1998/99 Outturn	1998/99 Plan	1997/98 Outturn
Number of sets of regulations introduced	19	17	8
Number of Approved Codes of Practice (ACoP) introduced	11	13	6
Number of consultative documents published	16	11	16
Number of new guidance documents published	16	25	26
Other	4	4	
Total	66	70	56
Percentage sets of regulations, ACoPs, consultative documents and guidance documents introduced to time.	82	88	84

Continuing aim 2: To secure compliance with the law in line with the principles of proportionality, consistency, transparency and targeting on a risk-related basis

Resources 1998/99				
Aim 2	Staff years	% Staff years	Staff costs £k	% Staff costs
Planned	1 936	53.3	61 046	54.2
Outturn	1 876	53.1	57 967	53.4

1.87   Inspection and other regulatory activity to secure compliance with the law are at the core of HSE's work. The law says that those who create the risks are responsible for ensuring that they are effectively controlled. Our task, and the task of local authorities who are also involved in health and safety enforcement, is to inform, stimulate, advise, guide and ensure compliance with the law. This year we continued with our policy of targeting our enforcement effort at those activities which present the greatest risk. We have responsibility for securing compliance in over 600 000 establishments covering around 13.2 million people. Local authorities enforce the Act in around 1 250 000 establishments, involving nearly ten million people.

1.88   Each year we receive around half a million requests for advice; make over 180 000 regulatory contacts which include: site visits, meetings between inspectors and managers and other operational contacts with duty holders; and investigate some 32 000 accidents, incidents and complaints. Similarly local authorities make regulatory contacts and investigate accidents and complaints in their enforcement sectors. Others with important roles in the health and safety system include employees and safety representatives, professional and voluntary organisations, insurance companies and health and safety consultants.

Increasing regulatory contacts

1.89   Our performance measure 'regulatory contacts' includes all the different types of inspection, investigation and other regulatory interventions which are undertaken in order to improve health and safety. This gives us greater flexibility to vary our response and use the most appropriate and effective methods. **We exceeded our target for the year, making 183 000 contacts** (see Table 4). Seminars, workshops and publicity campaigns are additional to regulatory contacts.

Table 4 Components of regulatory contacts for all inspectorates

Types of inspection/ investigation	Management data			
	1998/99 Outturn		1998/99 Planned/estimated	
	Number	% of total	Number/range	% of total
Preventive inspection	91 000	50	90 000 - 100 000	55 - 59
No. of visits to investigate accidents and complaints	44 500	25	38 000 - 40 000	22 - 24
Advisory visits (includes educational and promotional visits)	17 000	9	12 000 - 13 000	7 - 8
Enforcement visits (eg visits in connection with issue of enforcement notices or court attendances)	18 000	10	13 000 - 15 000	8 - 9
Visits in connection with special projects	2 500	1	2 000	1
Visits to manufacturers or suppliers (in connection with standards of new plants etc.)	2 000	1	2 000	1
Other	8 000	4	4 000	2
Total	**183 000**	100	**170 000**	100

Examples of activities during the year

1.90   We use a wide range of techniques to encourage compliance . Examples of initiatives carried out by FOD during the year, in addition to those mentioned in Section 1, included:

- a **quarries** safety day in the South East which focused on transport safety;

- an enforcement initiative against landlords in the private rented sector in the North West, following several examples of low levels of compliance with the **Gas** Safety (Installation and Use) Regulations;

- two seminars for Wales based **asbestos** removal contractors which attracted 95% of the target audience;

- over 1300 visits to duty holders in **fairgrounds and amusement parks** to ensure they have adequate arrangements in place to meet key recommendations in the new fairgrounds guidance;

- health and safety management inspections of over 30 **NHS trusts** to secure implementation of action plans to address non-compliance with legislation. This resulted in over 40 enforcement notices;

- an inspection initiative to **farms** open to the public to check standards of hygiene facilities and arrangements for public visitors;

- visits to over 70 **nursing homes** in Cornwall, resulting in 140 improvement notices and five prosecutions;

- sixty visits to **horse racing** establishments. As a result the industry arranged seminars and have included health and safety in the licensing conditions for trainers; and

- an initiative to enforce a full range of control measures against animal allergens in research laboratories. One university was prosecuted for several breaches of the **COSHH** Regulations following sensitisation of a research student in an animal house. This was the first case against an animal house operator for inadequate health surveillance.

Safety case regime

1.91   Our planned inspection programme works in conjunction with the safety case regime. Safety cases have been introduced in high-hazard industries and must be accepted or reviewed by HSE before certain operations may be undertaken. Safety cases or safety reports are required for offshore installations, nuclear installations, in the railways and gas industries and for certain onshore major hazard sites. Examples are given below of some of the initiatives carried out during the year in these industries.

Offshore industry

1.92   We published guidance *Assessment principles for offshore safety cases* which should ensure a better understanding of the principles against which HSE assessors evaluate the contents of safety cases submitted under the Offshore Installations (Safety Case) Regulations 1992. The industry trade associations and trades unions contributed to the development of the guidance.

1.93   All safety case assessments were completed within agreed time scales. The volume of assessment work reflected the requirement in the Regulations for resubmission after three years of previously accepted installation safety cases. As a result a total of 192 assessments were completed, a volume increase of approximately 30% over last year.

1.94   Important practical co-operation by five international regulators for the North Seas was achieved through the completion of the first ever 'Multinational Safety, Health and Environmental Management Audit' of a contractor operating mobile offshore drilling units. Offshore Safety Division (OSD) was a driving force behind the completion of this unique venture, which was undertaken by a team of inspectors from the offshore health and safety regulators in UK, Norway, Denmark, the Netherlands and Germany.

1.95   The success of this audit has been acknowledged by the drilling industry as a positive step in regulatory co-operation and has led to the commencement of a further audit with OSD leading the international team.

Nuclear installations

1.96   An in-depth audit of the management of safety at the United Kingdom Atomic Energy Authority (UKAEA) Dounreay was carried out by a joint HSE and Scottish Environment Protection Agency (SEPA) team in June 1998, initiated by HM Chief Inspector of Nuclear Installations. This followed an incident on 7 May 1998, which left the 'Fuel Cycle Area' on the site without its normal electricity supplies for 16 hours.

1.97   The report contained 143 recommendations, including the preparation by UKAEA of an Action Plan for agreement with HSE/SEPA by 30 November 1998. This was achieved, and since then, UKAEA have been working to progress the recommendations.

1.98   UKAEA have committed major resources to this work, and it remains a key area of work, with a substantial demand on the resources of the Nuclear Installations Inspectorate to monitor progress.

1.99   The assessments of the periodic safety reviews for Hartlepool and Heysham 1 nuclear power stations were completed and consent was given for their continued operation subject to a programme of modifications and further analysis.

1.100   The arrangements of nuclear licensees for storing Intermediate Level Waste were reviewed and a report published in December 1998.

Onshore major hazard sites

1.101   A programme of audits to assess health and safety management within major hazard industries included:

- a safety management systems audit of a petrochemical company which resulted in two prosecutions and an enforcement notice leading to significant changes in core procedures for risk assessment across the whole site's operations; and

- a detailed audit at a major refinery which revealed significant failings in the management of health and safety resulting in an improvement notice requiring substantial improvement to management systems. The findings came as a surprise to the company's most senior management who had, up until then, a totally different perception of the safety performance of the company.

1.102   HSE's Chemical and Hazardous Installations Division (CHID) has reviewed the way inspectors deal with multi-establishment companies and introduced a new system so that it can deal efficiently with the assessment of safety reports and in coordinating inspection plans for COMAH establishments. Consistency of approach has been improved by the development of guidance to inspectors on particular types of major hazard establishments.

Gas supply industry

1.103   The winter of 1998/99 was the first in which the market was open to full competition. CHID was involved in the arrangements between Ofgas and BG plc Transco to set out the latter's gas mains replacement strategy for the following three years.

1.104   A pilot has been carried out to review the standards of performance of gas conveyors who are not 'traditional' Public Gas Transporters with regard to maintenance of existing systems and construction of new ones, eg local authorities and owners of some industrial sites.

Railways

1.105   The Railway Inspectorate (RI) assessed the safety implications of the Government's plans for London Underground's (LU) public-private partnership (PPP) from early planning stages. RI continues to work in close liaison with LU on the development of the PPP model and the extent to which it supports health and safety arrangements. The PPP is expected to move into its next phase in 1999, with a "shadow running" period which informs the later bidding processes. RI also undertook some preliminary work to improve the processing, implementation and inspection of safety cases, including detailed discussion with Railtrack on the criteria for accepting safety cases. In total RI considered and agreed 260 safety cases and material revisions to safety cases. In addition a good deal of work went into the emerging requirements of London Underground's Jubilee Line Extension Project, both in terms of approving some of the novel processes and equipment, and scrutinising the new safety cases. The first part of the project - running from Stratford to North Greenwich - opened in April 1999.

1.106   The new works approval process continued to increase in line with the railway industry's expansion in investment. Ten train operating companies have ordered new trains, each of which is different and required detailed examination. Some have new or novel concepts, such as tilt, with associated new standards. Public expectation of new trains is, nowadays, much greater and this calls for increased effort on platform/train interface issues. RI gave approval for the Heathrow Express and the Midland Metro to start operations and has been closely involved in the development of safety issues in other major schemes, notably the Docklands Light Railway extension to Lewisham and the tramway at Croydon.

Enforcement

1.107   HSE and local authorities, the health and safety enforcing authorities, are required to take decisions on enforcement in accordance with the HSC's published Enforcement Policy Statement. Enforcement action must be proportionate to the risk, consistent, transparent and targeted on the most serious risks or where hazards are least well controlled.

1.108   In most cases, information, guidance and advice are sufficient to ensure that health and safety requirements are complied with. Where formal action is appropriate, the issue of an improvement or a prohibition notice normally provides a quick and effective means of securing the necessary improvements. The HSC expects, through its Enforcement Policy Statement, that enforcing authorities will consider prosecution when, for example, there is judged to have been the potential for serious harm arising from a breach, or when the gravity of a breach taken together with the general record and approach of the offender warrants it.

1.109   The protocol agreed with HSE, Crown Prosecution Service (CPS) and the Association of Chief Police Officers established procedures for responding to work-related deaths. Now more and more fatal accidents have involved joint investigations with the police and included discussions at various stages of the investigation with the CPS. The investigations are time consuming and often drawn out. The protocol will be extended to local authority enforcement through HELA and the Local Authority Associations.

Working in partnership with local authorities: consistency in enforcement

1.110   The Health and Safety Executive/Local Authorities Enforcement Liaison (HELA) commissioned quality assurance research on the management of consistency in enforcement within local authorities. The aim of the research was to identify key processes in local authorities which led to better management and quality assurance of the enforcement process. HELA considered the conclusions of this work and issued its response to local authorities in March 1999. It has decided as a priority to pursue recommendations on auditing, and the development of indicators of enforcement activity. HELA will continue with its work to identify and spread best practice.

Improvement and prohibition notices

1.111   Inspectors have the power to issue improvement notices (where specified improvements must be made within an agreed time period) or prohibition notices (where work must stop until specified actions are taken).

1.112   One aspect of the increasing impact of enforcement activity has been the number of appeals against notices which have been taken to hearings before employment tribunals - six last year compared with about one per year normally.

Penalties

1.113   The Commission has long been concerned that the general level of penalties imposed by the Courts does not match the real seriousness of health and safety offences, which can and do sometimes lead to terrible injury, ill health and death. Ministers and the HSC have welcomed the important November 1998 judgment in R v F Howe and Son (Engineers) Ltd. in which the Appeal Court said straightforwardly that health and safety fines are too low. The Appeal Court said that a fine must be large enough to bring home to those who manage a company, and their shareholders, the need for a safe environment for workers and the public; also that generally where death is the consequence of a criminal act it is regarded as an aggravating feature of the offence. The penalty should reflect public disquiet at the unnecessary loss of life. The Court of Appeal also identified a number of aggravating features which would be relevant when considering the gravity of future cases and set out factors which should underpin future sentencing. The decision of the Court of Appeal has resulted in a greater number of cases being committed to the Crown court for sentence - 13 in the first three months of 1999. The case provided the first clarification of the correct approach to sentencing for health and safety offences and a basis for inspectors drawing sentencing matters to the Court's attention.

1.114   Judges have already referred to this guidance in a number of cases: in one case the Norfolk and Norwich Health Trust was fined four times the previous average fine after a patient died as a result of poor systems of work; and following the Heathrow tunnel collapse, the main contractor, Balfour Beatty, was fined a record £1.2 million, and their subcontractor, Geoconsult GmBH, £0.5 million, plus £200 000 costs, for health and safety failures which put employees and the public at serious risk. Other recent cases also suggest that the Appeal Court guidance will have a strong positive effect on lower and higher court sentencing from now on.

However, the Commission continues to be concerned that the level of penalties for breaches of health and safety at work law is too low and intends to continue work, with Ministers and other authorities, to press this view.

1.115   The provisional figure for the average health and safety fines stood at £3179 between April and October last year, and increased to £6667 in November to March. A continued trend towards markedly higher penalties would be invaluable in bringing home the importance of complying with health and safety law, and deterring the minority whose cavalier attitude gives rise to special concern. We also welcome the message sent by the Courts, following a nine month jail sentence for putting employees and public at risk from illegal work with asbestos. Failure to control properly such risks is a serious offence, sometimes made all the more repugnant when corners are cut for profit.

Prosecutions

1.116   The following are examples of some of prosecutions completed during 1998/99:

- Following an investigation of a fire in August 1996, in which two workers died in a Glasgow adhesives factory, the company has been prosecuted and fined a total of £100 000. In addition, the managing director was convicted of personal negligence and fined £7000.

- In 1996 a mix up in paperwork resulted in the wrong chemical being delivered to a major chemical plant where it was off-loaded into storage vessels containing an incompatible material. This caused a violent exothermic reaction and an explosion. A number of people were injured and a cloud of toxic fume and smoke drifted off site causing the temporary closure of nearby motorways and the Severn river crossing. The chemicals company which received the chemical and a Belgium haulage company. were fined £75 000 and ordered to pay costs of £35 000.

- In February 1999 the first ever prosecutions under the Genetically Modified Organisms (Contained Use) and (Deliberate Release) Regulations were taken. In one case a University was fined £35 000 after pleading guilty to failing to carry out suitable risk assessments for activities involving genetic modifications at the University's Medical school.   In the same month two companies were fined £17 000 and £14 000 respectively and ordered to pay costs of £6160 and £5000 for failing to ensure that field trials of genetically modified winter oilseed rape were conducted in line with the conditions of their consents.

- Cases were taken against two defendants in the waste paper sector following a major injury accident when an HGV driver fell from the top of a loaded trailer in the waste paper sector. Fines totalling £20 000 were imposed in the magistrates' court and the cases have had major impact in the industry.

- A local scaffolding firm was prosecuted and fined £15 000 following the sudden and catastrophic collapse of an extensive scaffold as it was being dismantled within the auditorium of a theatre. Six men working on the scaffold were lucky to escape with their lives as they were thrown to the circle balcony some 30 feet below - four of them suffered serious injury.

- A tyre manufacturer was fined £100 000 following the death of a 28 year old calender operator. The operator was taken into an in - running nip and was crushed. Investigation showed major failures with respect to provision of safe plant, safe systems of work, instructions, training and supervision.

- A large supermarket chain in Basingstoke was prosecuted by the local authority and fined £425 000 following the death of a worker when a fork-lift truck overturned.

Incidents and investigations

1.117   HSE has developed new procedures for how it responds to and investigates major incidents, reports of which will be made publicly available. Major incidents are high profile events and HSE has to respond appropriately and be seen by the public to be responding. Major investigations and incidents requiring immediate attention demand a considerable amount of our time and effort. Examples of the range of investigations we carry out include:

- the investigation of two major acid leakages at a chemical waste company. In May 1998, approximately 10 tonnes of concentrated mixed acid leaked from a road tanker when the rear door seal failed and later that month a glass reinforced plastic storage tank split open and released approximately 14 tonnes of waste acid. As a result of the investigation prosecutions have been initiated by HSE and by the Environment Agency; and

- the investigation of an incident at a large bakery in which two men died from heat exhaustion whilst carrying out maintenance work. A large scale joint police/HSE investigation was mounted. CPS have decided against preferring manslaughter charges but HSE are taking cases against both corporate bodies and a number of directors and managers.

1.118   Both the above investigations involved staff from the Health and Safety Laboratory (HSL) and consumed significant amounts of HSE resource.

1.119   A very different kind of investigation was carried out into the supply of non-approved imported pesticides by a farming company. This ground breaking work involved obtaining a warrant to enter domestic premises and search for relevant documentation, in addition to empowering named inspectors to seize pesticides on behalf of the Executive. Non-approved pesticides were seized from the supplying company and also from farmers who had been supplied with and used such pesticides.

1.120   HSE's investigation into the railway accident at Southall in September 1997, in which seven people died, was carried out jointly with British Transport Police. The ensuing prosecution of Great Western Trains Company Limited for an offence under Section 3 (1) of the HSW etc Act resulted in the company pleading guilty and being fined £1.5 million.

1.121   A public inquiry into the Southall accident was opened in February 1998 and adjourned pending completion of criminal proceedings. The inquiry, conducted under the HSW etc Act Section 14(2)(b), reopened on 20 September 1999 and will conclude in November 1999. The Inquiry Chairman will report to the Health and Safety Commission in the New Year.

1.122   The Railway Inspectorate published its reports and recommendations following accidents at Watford and Bexley, which occurred respectively on 8 August 1996 and 4 February 1997. It also published its findings on the derailment of a freight train conveying dangerous goods at Barry on 27 December 1997. As a result of this accident, South Wales Police evacuated about 1000 local residents from their homes. Nobody was injured in the accident.

Investigation of incidents

We investigate incidents to learn lessons and influence the law and guidance; to prevent them happening again and to put gross breaches before the courts. HSE will carry out a site investigation of a reported workplace death, unless there are specific circumstances such as deaths on railways where the British Transport Police regard the event as suicide.

In selecting which of the many thousands of reports of major injuries to investigate an inspector close to the circumstance will consider:

- the actual and potential severity of the event;
- the seriousness of any potential breach of the law;
- the track record of the duty holder;
- enforcement priorities both national and local;
- the practicality of achieving results; and
- the relevance of the event to a wider range of premises.

Working Time Directive

1.123   The Working Time Regulations 1998, implementing the Working Time and the Young Workers Directive, came into force in October 1998. Policy responsibility rests with DTI, but HSE and local authorities have responsibility for enforcing the working time limits and night work restrictions. HSE has appointed Working Time Officers (WTOs), one located within each FOD region, to handle queries on the Regulations. Since the beginning of October 1998, WTOs have received about 10 000 enquiries and have logged 110 complaints which are at various stages of investigation. So far, none of these has led to formal enforcement.

Improving the quality of information

1.124   Obtaining timely information of accidents and cases of ill health is vital to the operational capability of HSE and local authorities. During 1998/99 we began a study to assess the feasibility of applying a range of new technology options to make the reporting of accidents easier for business under the Reporting of Injuries, Diseases and Dangerous Occurrences Regulations 1995 (RIDDOR).

1.125   The study builds on the success of the telephone reporting pilot in Scotland, which won a Government Computing Award for Innovation during 1998. The study reported in May 1999 and identified a very favourable reaction from businesses which had used the service. We are taking forward a project in co-operation with local authorities, to introduce a single national call centre reporting system which allows the options of reporting to a single point by telephone, the Internet or paper. This would enable HSE to exceed the Government's 25% delivery target for statutory notifications.

1.126   We have carried out research into hospital treatment of work-related injuries to establish, with more precision, the nature and extent of under-reporting of RIDDOR injuries by employers. Preliminary results indicate that employers do not report, in particular, injuries which require a change of normal duties (rather than absence from the workplace) and major injuries which require less than four days absence from work. Full results will be published in 1999/2000.

Key outputs

1.127   We investigated some 5.7% of all injuries and incidents notified to us in 1998/99, which is less than the planned figure of 6.1%. We fell just short of the target, in part because of the diversion of investigatory effort towards dealing with the higher than expected number of complaints - 29 500 were reported to us, 7000 more than we had forecast. There was also a shift in activity to enforcement action - over 20% more improvement and prohibition notices were issued than in the previous year.

1.128   1998/99 was the first year of FOD's quality and improvement programme which aims to standardise key procedures, to be more consistent, free up inspector time and maximise the potential of administrative staff. One of the quality procedures which has been established and implemented is the Complaints Handling System - how to process and prioritise the ever-rising volume of complaints.

1.129   Inspectors spent 78% of available inspector time in direct contact with clients and related activities, such as travel to site and office follow up. This fell below our target of 80%. This measure reflects the proportion of time spent by operational inspectors producing field outputs, such as inspections, investigations and prosecutions; it includes the associated office time devoted to managing and processing such work. This target is deliberately set high so as to provide a challenge to our operating directorates/divisions. We had hoped that our business improvement programmes would have led to an increase in contact time with duty holders. But the anticipated benefits from these programmes did not come through as quickly as expected. This dip in performance is therefore considered to be only temporary in nature.

Key outputs and quality measures	1998/99 Outturn	1998/99 Plan	1997/98 Outturn
Regulatory contacts, including inspections and investigations, with employers and duty holders	183 292	170 000	186 065
Incidents/complaints investigated	32 270	29 000	33 585
Safety cases and nuclear licence actions processed	759	740	658
% high hazard/risk workplaces receiving annual inspection contact (excludes CHID and RI who use an alternative systematic appraisal of hazards/risks)	96	100	100
% reported events (injuries/incidents) investigated	5.7	6.1	6.9
% complaints (about work activities) investigated	77	85	74
% safety assessments and nuclear licence actions processed to time	89	87	90
% prosecutions resulting in convictions	83P	+	79
Number of enforcement notices issued	10 844P	8 500	8 812
Number of prosecutions	1 797P	1 900	1 654
% inspector time spent on site/contact and related activities (as proportion of total time available)	78	80	79

Note:

+	*Targets not set*
P	*Provisional*

Continuing aim 3: To improve the knowledge and understanding of health and safety through the provision of appropriate and timely information and advice

Resources 1998/99				
Aim 3	Staff years	% Staff years	Staff costs £k	% Staff costs
Planned	316	8.7	9 977	8.8
Outturn	321	9.1	9 947	9.2

1.130   Providing information and advice about the hazards and risks that arise from work activities is a core activity which is vital to our effectiveness. Information and advice get across important messages on health and safety to a far greater number of employers, employees and members of the public than we could ever hope to reach through inspection alone. The integration of inspection and information is a powerful tool.

Electronic services

1.131   The **HSE web site was expanded with over 2 500 pages attracting over 75 000 'hits' a week.** The programme to add all HSE's free publications was a major factor in the increased access and use of the site. We have developed an electronic catalogue on the web site, which is being tested. It will be possible to: search this in various ways, for example by topic; see a photo of the cover of the document; read a précis of the content - so that the customer can select the most relevant book; and place an order over the Internet. A seamless link will connect our commercial site and our main HSE site.

1.132   We have continued to produce a range of electronic publications, such as HSELINE on-line, in partnership with private organisations, in order to give people access to the information they want in the way they want it. Interactive CD ROMs include the prize-winning *Welding fume tutor* which won second prize in the multimedia competition in Sao Paolo.

1.133   HSE's input to Direct Access Government (DAG) - electronic access to services and information, and helplines - continued and HSE was amongst the principal providers of information to DAG.

Services to the public

1.134   **InfoLine** - an enquiry and reference service - managed more calls and enquiries than ever before, some 222 000 in the year, about half of them from small and medium-size firms. A customer evaluation of InfoLine at the end of 1998 demonstrated that callers had high expectations of the service which were fully justified. Over 90% of all InfoLine callers were satisfied or very satisfied with the service.

1.135   The expansion of the Internet services and the success of InfoLine resulted in the closure of the HSE Autofax service in March 1999. Autofax was handling fewer and fewer calls and had outlived its value.

1.136   We have introduced a minicom service for the deaf at our Information Centre in Bootle so that staff and members of public who are hard of hearing can receive messages.

1.137   A list of our publications during the year is given in Annex 4. They include guidance for local authority enforced sectors, including *Health and safety at motor sports events - a guide for employers and organisers* which has been commended by the Plain Language Commission for its clarity and all-round excellence. Our aim is always to provide information in a way which can be easily understood by its target audience.

Provision of safety, ill health and enforcement statistics

1.138   We compile, interpret and publish safety, ill health and enforcement statistics in *Health and safety statistics* and in the *HSC Annual Report and accounts*. The figures allow HSE to consider its operational priorities and redirect field resources if necessary. They also contribute to openness and inform general debate on health and safety issues. This year, for the first time, we released in-year quarterly statistics (published in November and February) on to the Internet.

1.139   Injury, ill health and enforcement statistics for the local authority enforced sectors are published in the *HELA National picture of health and safety in the local authority enforced sectors 1999*. In July 1998 we also published a series of fact sheets on reported injuries in the local authority enforced sectors.

1.140   *Health and safety statistics* also contains the results of the 1996/97 Labour Force Survey, a questionnaire on heath and safety which supplements data from RIDDOR reportable accidents. These show a gradual improvement by employers on reporting non-fatal injuries leading to four or more days absence. The Labour Force Survey shows that the rate of injury reportable to HSE or local authorities is dropping gradually.

1.141   Research has been carried out with WS Atkins to show the relationship between the costs of accidents and their causes. The results will be published in autumn 1999.

The Millennium Bug

1.142   HSE continues to pursue its four-pronged strategy for tackling the potential risks to safety from the **Millennium Bug**. This comprises research, awareness raising, co-operation with other bodies and enforcement. HSE followed up the research report *Safety and the year 2000,* published in January 1998, with four more publications:

- a free leaflet *Health and safety and the year 2000,* published in April 1998;

- *Testing safety-related control systems for year 2000 compliance,* published in August 1998;

- two free leaflets *Contingency planning for a safe year 2000,* published in November 1998; and *Year 2000 risk,* published in January 1999;

- HSE also published in late 1998 a report of a survey *Major hazards sites and the millennium problem.*

1.143   HSE launched a major advertising campaign in early 1999 to draw employers' attention to Millennium Bug safety risks. We worked actively with the Cabinet Office and Action 2000 initiatives, and used the levers available under permissioning or licensing régimes in high-risk industries to ensure that firms take adequate measures to control Millennium Bug risks. Preparations were put in place for a National Project on the Millennium Bug by the Field Operations Directorate (FOD) with 250 targeted visits per region between April and October 1999. FOD and local authority inspectors have also been raising Millennium Bug safety issues during the first of their inspections to individual premises from 1 January 1999.

Key outputs and quality measures	1998/99 Outturn	1998/99 Plan	1997/98 Outturn
Number of enquiries handled	476 499	550 000	448 000
Number (range) of publicity products made available, eg titles, Internet pages and press conferences	4 489	2 100	2 707
Number of publicity products consumed, (eg free leaflets, priced publications), including: - Internet 'hits'*	11 577 599 2 385 970	7 700 000 800 000	7 352 142 400 000
% of public enquiries answered within 10 days	97	100	97
% customer satisfaction with HSE service†	79	+	86
Number of justified or partly justified complaints against HSE staff per 100 000 contacts	5	+	6

Notes:

+   Targets not set.

*   The trend in this output illustrates the tremendous expansion in the use of the Internet to access information.

†   Customer satisfaction is measured by a two year rolling survey across HSE's FOD regions. On average, over the two years, 82% indicated they were satisfied with the service they received. One region was significantly below the average and the reasons for this are being investigated.

Continuing aim 4: To promote risk assessment and technological knowledge as the basis for setting standards and guiding enforcement activities

Resources 1998/99				
Aim 4	Staff years	% Staff years	Staff costs £k	% Staff costs
Planned	189	5.2	6 676	5.9
Outturn	181	5.1	6 284	5.8

1.144   Our mission to ensure that risks to people's health and safety from industrial activities are properly controlled requires a thorough knowledge and understanding of science and technology related to health and safety evaluation and the prevention of accidents and ill health. We are responsible for a large part of the national store of hazard experience and for keeping this knowledge up to date as technology advances. This intelligence is used in proposing regulations and standards proportionate to the risks, in advice and guidance to industry and in enforcement.

1.145   We provide essential contributions to health and safety developments nationally and internationally, for example providing technical input to the negotiation of directives and standards and sound economic appraisal across all areas.

1.146   Our work on *Technology trends* has provided the forward looking element essential for anticipating future demands. The establishment of a robust HSE database of developing technological trends and their implications for health and safety provides a snapshot in time of the continuously changing scene of technology. It was published as an open discussion document in spring 1998 and put on HSE's web site.

Research

1.147   HSE's mainstream research programme is concerned with safety, hygiene and health risks arising from work activities. In 1999/2000, HSE plans to spend about £21 million on research in addition to research funded through HSE by industry. HSE's annual *Mainstream research market* document for 1999/2000 was published in February 1999. It states how the research is procured and managed and defines the way in which the future trends in HSE's research requirements are gauged. It is aimed primarily at providing information on and raising general awareness of HSE's current research activities and anticipated research requirements.

1.148   The document is also intended to stimulate opportunities for collaboration. Following on from the success of last year's document it again features a 'Competition of Ideas' exercise aimed at stimulating new ideas for research in response to identified broad issues facing HSE.

1.149   HSE is committed to procuring its research in a rigorous competitive regime which provides value for money. We place a high priority on collaborative partnerships and increasing competition, leading to better use of resources and improved outcomes. Our Ministerial targets on collaborations for 1998/9 were for 30% of new projects to involve others - which we exceeded - and 40% of new contracts to be put out to tender.

1.150   Examples of research projects include:

- an examination of issues concerning the integrity of **Mark 1 rolling stock** arising from numerous railway accidents. Results of the research allow relatively cheap modification until all of the stock is replaced in 2005. A report was published in August 1999;

- research into **respirable dust** commissioned from the Institute of Occupational Medicine, Edinburgh, which has shed new light on the harmful properties of respirable particles. The Institute of Environment and Health has also published the outcome of an international workshop which we commissioned to draw together emerging views on what causes these fine particles to be so harmful. This will feed into standards setting and advice on control;

- publication of a contract research report with a widely consulted methodology for identifying **hand-arm vibration** (HAV), which should encourage better and more consistent diagnosis of HAV. Dealing with the harmful effects of HAV has been hindered by the lack of agreed diagnostic methodologies;

- publication of three contract research reports on **psychosocial issues** - one on organisational interventions to prevent stress and two on post-incident trauma. We commissioned further research on the evaluation of stress auditing techniques; the effects of new ways of working such as 'hot desking' and aspirations to be a learning organisation on employee stress levels; and the scale of violence at work; and

- completion of a successful pilot study on the health of **agricultural pesticide users**. The data will be made widely available to other researchers as well as meeting HSE's needs.

Scientific activities of advisory committees

1.151   The Commission is well supported by advisory committees which bring together individuals with considerable scientific background and standing in their fields. These committees analyse and review specific issues from an essentially scientific viewpoint as a contribution to the broader formulation of policy. Such activities include:

- **Advisory Committee on Toxic Substances (ACTS)** review programme. ACTS considered over 40 papers on the effects of industrial substances on human health. It was also reconstituted with a broader membership to reflect a still wider range of expertise. The participation of people representing all parts of industry, academic expertise, environmental and public interest, and observers from other government departments, in decisions on risk assessment and management of substances ensures the quality of debate is wide ranging and rigorous. Occupational exposure limits and other risk management options were agreed by those who make and face the risk.

- **Advisory Committee on Genetic Modification (ACGM).** ACGM advised on the development of proposals for a major revision of the legislation on contained use of genetically modified organisms. These would bring the legislation in line with scientific developments, establish improved procedures for conducting risk assessments, and make the notification requirements which inform enforcement activity more soundly risk-based. During the year, ACGM's Technical Sub Committee considered a number of specific risk assessments notified under the current legislation. Substantial progress was also made with the revision of ACGM's Compendium of Guidance which offers detailed advice, reflecting technological developments, on risk assessment and the appropriate control of various types of genetic modification activities.

- **Advisory Committee on Dangerous Pathogens (ACDP).** ACDP has been reconstituted and the membership represents a wide range of expertise and considerable experience in most aspects of microbiology and infectious diseases, including epidemiological expertise. The Committee continues to apply the principles of microbiological risk assessment in giving advice on issues such as the classification of new and emerging biological agents and in considering the infectious disease risks associated with new technologies such as xenotransplantation.

Risk assessment

1.152   A discussion document *Reducing risks, protecting people* was published in May 1999. This explains how, as a regulator, we decide on the balance between risk and benefits, describing the principles, protocols, processes and criteria that we adopt when reaching such decisions, and embracing the complete spectrum of harms we regulate.

Key outputs and quality measures	1998/99 Outturn	1998/99 Plan	1997/98 Outturn
Number of research contracts let	309	300	340
Number of research projects which involve external collaborators	123	85	87
% research projects completed to time	95	95	95
Number of risk and technical policy projects	126	120	*
% risk and technical policy projects done to time	79	70	*

Note:

*   *New measure, comparative figures not available.*

Continuing aim 5: To operate statutory schemes, including regulatory services, through, for example, the Employment Medical Advisory Service

Resources 1998/99				
Aim 5	Staff years	% Staff years	Staff costs £k	% Staff costs
Planned	155	4.3	4 373	3.9
Outturn	143	4.0	3 827	3.5

1.153   Our statutory functions include the provision of statutory schemes to industry and the public to ensure that particular products, substances or activities are assessed, approved or certified by the Government before they are marketed. This involves testing, certification and approval work.

1.154   We have a major role to play in controls on the **supply of chemicals** to the market through risk assessment work. Permissioning and approvals work is part of this continuing aim and ensures that new chemical substances and non-agricultural pesticides do not pose an unacceptable risk to people or the environment. This work involves critical evaluation of test data supplied by industry which informs decisions taken on behalf of the European Union (for new substances) and by Ministers (for non-agricultural pesticides).

1.155   These continuing, statutory schemes are demand-driven. HSE has to complete the appraisal work before supply can take place. In the case of new substances, these are statutory deadlines; with pesticides we agree demanding performance targets with the users, who are charged for the work. During the year, despite very considerable pressure on these schemes, the targets that most directly affect businesses have been met without compromising health and safety.

1.156   Our medical inspectors and occupational health inspectors play an important role in our inspection programme and provide medical surveillance of workers exposed to specific hazards such as lead, asbestos and diving and also carry out investigations of occupational health problems. As the **Employment Medical Advisory Service** (EMAS) they provide a wide range of occupational health advice to employers, employees, the public and health professionals. They also provide information and evidence to the courts in connection with civil claims and public enquiries. In 1998/99 EMAS have been developing the role of medical and occupational health inspectors across HSE's divisions and directorates and with the local authorities' Environmental Health Officers.

1.157   EMAS also manages the appointed doctor system for carrying out statutory medical surveillance where an audit system has been introduced, to ensure that work is carried out to a satisfactory standard. Lectures, presentations and research projects have also been completed for the Good Health is Good Business campaign and research and discussion papers published in peer reviewed and trade journals.

1.158   The **Electrical Equipment Certification Service** (EECS) provides assurance that explosion-protected equipment is designed and manufactured in conformity with appropriate safety standards through type examination and the licensing of the use of registered certification trade marks. It also participates in the creation and development of safety standards for explosion-protected equipment. EECS aims to provide an efficient and cost-effective certification service to manufacturers and users of explosion-protected equipment and ensures that the service is responsive to technological developments. In 1998/99 EECS introduced a 'fixed price' quotations system. Work is continuing on implementing and offering to all customers options to pay by various means. It has continued to review all its services and has introduced a 'customer survey questionnaire' in order to establish its customers views of the services offered.

Key outputs and quality measures	1998/99 Outturn	1998/99 Plan	1997/98 Outturn
Number of service products:			
Exemptions issued by MI	348	285	401
Approvals issued by MI	10	15	13
Diving certificates issued	900	750	800
Mining qualification certificates issued	43	80	52
Jobs completed by Electrical Equipment Certification Service	1 172	1 252	1 191
Explosive classifications dealt with by CHID	324	290	292
Major hazard consents/plans issued by CHID	53	50	98
Pesticide approvals by HD	260	212	197
Notification of new substances (HD)	143	130	327
Genetic modification notifications processed by DST	249	190	263
Asbestos licence applications processed	332	300	584
Total	3 834	3 554	4 218
% of service products processed to time	94	88	90

Notes:

MI   Mines Inspectorate

CHID   Chemical and Hazardous Installations Division

HD   Health Directorate

DST   Directorate of Science and Technology

Section 3

Managing the organisation

Internal management aim: To maintain an efficient and effective central service which promotes and secures value for money.

Efficiency measures and initiatives

1.159   HSE continued its wide ranging programme of efficiency and business improvement work. This year we achieved quantified efficiency gains (cash savings and output gains) of over £5 million. Although a creditable achievement, representing a saving of 3% of running costs, it was slightly below target. This reflects the progressively more demanding nature of the task of identifying scope for efficiency. The development of HSE's business improvement programme should enable us to meet that challenge

1.160   Increasingly, divisions and directorates are putting quality programmes in place which systematically review the main business processes through which HSE delivers its mission. Quality projects and improvement reviews have a strong productivity effect e.g increasing inspector contact time and improving HSE accessibility and service standards e.g telephone call handling.

1.161   All of HSE's services and activities are in scope of the business improvement strategy. This year the core policy function was reviewed and this identified process improvements in the way policy work is planned and managed. Reviews of the administrative function in the Operations Group strengthened the quality of business support to HSE specialists.

1.162   Implementation of the Efficiency Study of Research Commissioning achieved substantial efficiency gains of over £250 000 as HSE merged units responsible for research administration and moved to a single approval/contracting process model.

1.163   Other projects included the contracting out of short-term administrative appointments enabling HSE to optimise the development and deployment of our key support staff. These staff make a crucial difference to the efficiency of HSE by increasingly providing an operational contribution as we continue to reduce unnecessary bureaucracy and introduce quality systems.

1.164   Bearing down on the central overhead continues to be an important part of the efficiency strategy. A business process re-engineering review of HSE's finance processes was completed and implementation is in hand. A similarly comprehensive review of the personnel process and systems enabled effort to be switched to new priorities.

Table 5   Costed efficiency gains - 1998/99

Nature of efficiency or economy measure	Outturn £million	Target £million
Management and staff reviews	2.8	3.0
Gains from the introduction of information technology including telecommunications equipment	0.3	0.4
Corporate economy measures	1.5	1.5
All other efficiency measures (including gains in purchasing, travel economies, energy savings)	0.7	1.6
Total	**5.3**	**6.5**

Resources

1.165   In 1998/99 HSE achieved a net expenditure within 0.2% of its provision.. Table 6 shows the provision and expenditure in 1998/99 and expenditure in 1997/98. A more detailed analysis is given in note 19 to the Accounts, page 158.

1.166   In autumn 1998, following the Government's Comprehensive Spending Review, HSC were given an extra £63 million in running costs to be spread over the next three years. The settlement is dependent, in part, on the extension of the Commission's existing charging regime for permissioning activities (see paragraphs 1.192 and 1.193).

Table 6   Financial provision

	1997/98 Outturn	1998/99 Final provision	£ thousands 1998/99 Outturn
Running costs	161 277	164 085	163 896
Capital expenditure	6 998	7 450	8 221
Other current expenditure	49 767	48 331	48 061
Gross total	218 042	219 866	220 178
Health and Safety Laboratory Agency (net)	-1 990	1 444	-2 499
Receipts	-39 445	-39 082	-38 902
Net grant in aid	176 607	182 228	178 777

Note: The figures include recoverable VAT on contracted running costs services. A more detailed analysis is given in note 19 to the Accounts (page 158).

Staffing

1.167   The HSC Plan of Work 1998/99 gave a planned staffing figure of 3977 at 1 April 1999. In the event the total staffing was 3880, ie 97 below the original plan. This was due to some recruitment lags and managing towards expected levels in 1999/00. Actual staffing levels, by occupational group, are given in tables 7 and 8.

Table 7 Total HSC/E staff in post by occupational group

	1.4.97 Staff in post	1.4.98 Staff in post	1.4.99 Staff in post
Inspectors*	1 442	1 437	1 497
Other professional or specialist staff	1 223	1 233	1 244
Other staff	1 412	1 262	1 139
Total staff	4 077	3 932	3 880

Note:

*   Table includes inspectors on non-inspection duties (eg line management, contributing to policy or technical standards).

1.168   In 1998/99 HSE (excluding the Health and Safety Laboratory) deployed a total human resource of 3536 staff years, ie the equivalent of this number of people working a full year. Figure 1 below shows how these resources were allocated between each of our main continuing aims and gives a comparison with planned staffing levels. This type of analysis, including the derived staff payroll costs, enables HSE to produce its Resource Accounts according to Treasury's new accounting requirements.

Figure 1 Deployment of staff resources

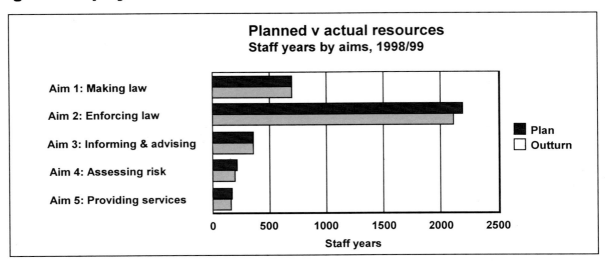

Note:

Aim 2: Despite inspector numbers increasing by 60 in-year, the staff resources devoted to Aim 2 still fell below target. This is mainly because of difficulties in recruiting specialist inspectors.

Table 8 Staff in post by division

	1.4.97	1.4.98	1.4.99
	Staff in post	Staff in post	Staff in post
Health and Safety Commission (HSC) (Support) and Senior Management Support Unit (SMSU)*	34	32	32
Solicitor's Office	19	20	20
Policy Unit (and Training Initiative)	42	43	42
Resources and Planning Directorate	564	553	507
Health Directorate	257	255	250
Safety Policy Directorate	141	144	144
Operations Group			
Operations Unit	25	24	20
Local Authority Unit	21	19	17
Field Operations Directorate	1 565	1 420	1 415
Chemical and Hazardous Installations Division	208	237	271
HM Railway Inspectorate	88	89	97
HM Inspectorate of Mines	41	40	35
Offshore Safety Division	257	254	237
Nuclear Safety Directorate	245	241	224
Directorate of Science and Technology	163	158	167
Electrical Equipment Certification Service	55	53	51
Total HSE staff	**3 725**	**3 582**	**3 529**
Health and Safety Laboratory	352	351	351
Total staff	**4 077**	**3 932**	**3 880**

Note:

*   *HSC (Support) and SMSU merged in September/October 1998. HSC (Support) was 5 staff in post at 1 April 1997 and 1 April 1998.*

Recruitment

1.169   Recruitment into the Health and Safety Executive is conducted in accordance with the Civil Service Commissioners Recruitment Code. The Executive operates systems and procedures which meet the requirements of the Code and these are subject to periodic internal and external audits. The Code requires departments to publish summary information about their recruitment and the use of permitted exceptions to the principles of fair and open competition and selection on merit. The required information is set out in Table 9 below.

1.170   During the year, 232 permanent staff and 152 casual temporary staff were recruited. The exceptions to the principles are 61 casual appointments beyond 12 months due to the unforeseen continuation of projects and restructuring programmes.

Table 9 Staff recruitment

Recruitment level	Number	Male	Female	White	Non-white	Disabled
Band 0						
Band 1						
Band 2	1	0	1	1	0	0
Band 3	57	46	11	52	4	0
Band 4	88	42	46	80	2	0
Band 5	21	8	13	11	9	1
Band 6	217	104	113	183	17	3
Total	384	200	184	327	32	4

Notes:

The job band structure replaces both the traditional Civil Service grades and HSE-managed grades. The structure enables HSE to be more flexible in managing its resources to ensure that its business needs are met.

The apparent discrepancy in the total of 'Whites' and ' Non-whites' is due to 25 recruits not declaring their ethnic origin..

Management initiatives

Initiative: To develop quality management principles and approaches as appropriate

1.171   A quality policy for HSE's core processes is now in place and will shortly be underpinned by a series of quality statements, one for each of HSC/E's continuing aims.

Initiative: To apply 'Investors in People' principles and activities to achieve IiP status

1.172   By the end of March 1999, all parts of HSE had gained recognition as **Investors in People** (IiP), the national training and development standard. This is the culmination of HSE's strategy for achieving IiP on a phased basis by 1998, and is in line with the Government's target for all departments to achieve recognition by the Year 2000.

Initiative: To take action on equal opportunities

1.173   During the year we:

• continued to review equal opportunities policies and developed an approach to "Diversity and Equality". Notable results included the HSE Board participating in a valuing diversity workshop; a commitment by the Executive to Managing and Valuing Diversity; and a series of staff focus meetings to explore and discuss valuing diversity;

• took action to reinforce equality of opportunity in recruitment, internal vacancy filling and promotion procedures. This included placing greater emphasis on diversity in our recruitment strategy; training recruitment assessors in equal opportunities issues; ensuring diverse membership of interview panels; and maintaining a high profile for part-time and job share arrangements for internal vacancies;

• continued work on the ethnic minority agenda for action which included an equality audit on the performance appraisal system; increased participation in the Windsor Fellowship Scheme; holding seminars across HSE to promote discussion on ethnic minority issues; and

• published revised guidance on sexual and racial harassment and issued guidance on unacceptable behaviour.

Health and safety of staff

1.174   To help to deliver its policy of setting and maintaining exemplary standards of health and safety performance, HSE produced a three-year Corporate Health and Safety Plan for 1998/2001. This introduced a number of continuing aims and four priority objectives for risk control. The plan supports the health and safety management system revised in the previous year, and gives HSE managers a framework for improving performance.

1.175   Priorities for 1998/99 were:

• to ensure that the significant findings from risk assessments and control measures are recorded and acted upon;

• to ensure that monitoring arrangements for health and safety performances are in place, understood and carried out;

• to tackle the causes of work-related upper limb disorder; and

• to evaluate work related stressors and develop solutions.

1.176   Directorates and free-standing divisions addressed the aims and priorities in their own plans. They reported at the half year and end of year to the Board which monitors performance both by measuring progress against plans and by analysis of accident, injury and ill health data.

1.177   In 1998/99 there were 373 internal reports covering accidents, ill health and near misses, 20 fewer than 97/98. But ill health notifications rose 30% in 98/99 to 132, the majority being suspected work-related upper limb disorder (WRULD) involving display screen equipment use. In line with the priority in the corporate plan, directorates have committed significant resources to prevention of WRULD.

1.178   The number of incidents reportable under RIDDOR fell to 12 (19 in 97/98) in relation to HSE employees and to one (two in 97/98) relating to a contractor working on HSE premises. RIDDOR reports on HSE employees covered: two major injuries; three cases of ill health each involving work with display screen equipment; five over-3-day injuries mainly involving slips trips and falls; and two dangerous occurrences, one from a fire started by welding and the other from an electrical fault.

1.179   In 1998 there was a total of 47 000 working days lost in HSE through sickness absence - an average of 11.7 days per person. Within that figure, at least 800 working days were lost through incidents at work and ill health brought on by work activity - representing a salary cost to the organisation of some £200 000. HSE is committed to measures to reduce total sickness absence in HSE by 20% by 2001, including plans to tackle the main cause of incidents and ill health arising from work.

1.180   The national major and over-3-day injury incidence rates for office-based activities are estimated to be about 600 per 100 000 employees, around five times greater than those in HSE.

HSE's commitment to government initiatives

Greening of HSE

1.181   HSE continued to pursue and promote best environmental practice across its estate and has planned further initiatives set out in the model policy statement issued by the Department of the Environment, Transport and the Regions (DETR). Actions included:

*   continued development of a green housekeeping strategy. An internal policy statement on Greening HSE is now ready for issue;

*   the establishment of a Green Team to develop, review and monitor a programme for improving the environmental impact of HSE's operation. The Green Team will lead all green initiatives and co-ordinate a system of green representatives who will be responsible for ensuring that relevant initiatives are given proper attention in their part of the organisation;

*   ensuring that those responsible for HSE's purchasing policy are aware of the environmental implications of purchasing practices and policies; and

- HSE's energy consumption remains on course to meet the 20% target reductions against the 1991 baseline figure by March 2001.

Citizen's Charter/Service First

1.182   Service First, the new Charter programme, was launched in June 1998 to replace Citizen's Charter. HSE is committed to the new Charter programme and our revised Charter booklets will reflect the nine new principles of public service delivery introduced by Service First.

1.183   As part of our Charter we monitor our performance in answering enquiries and levels of customer satisfaction. In 1998/99, we received over 476 000 enquiries, including over 222 000 calls to HSE's InfoLine, a helpline to deal with enquiries from individuals about health and safety in the workplace. Eighty percent of calls to InfoLine were answered within 15 seconds. Monitoring of our main regulatory customer interface shows that 79% of customers were satisfied with HSE's services. One of the FOD regions was significantly below the average and the reasons for this are being investigated.

1.184   We investigate all complaints made against HSE staff and in 1998/99 we received 91 complaints, compared with 117 in 1997/98. Of these, 35 were found to be justified or partly justified.

Freedom of information

1.185   Because of delays to the commencement of the Data Protection Act 1998 and in the preparation of freedom of information legislation, systems for meeting the new requirements have not been activated. Nevertheless all directorates and divisions within HSE have drawn up data protection implementation plans and are ready to put them into operation as soon as the Act comes into force. HSC/E has also made a positive contribution to the development of freedom of information legislation and HSE has embarked on a policy project to ensure that it is ready to implement new freedom of information requirements. In the meantime HSC/E continues to make information available under the Code of Practice on Access to Government Information and the Environmental Information Regulations 1992 in line with HSC's policy.

Welsh language scheme

1.186   Under the Welsh Language Act 1993, HSE is required to establish a scheme for the promotion of the Welsh language. This was approved by the Welsh Language Board in April 1997. The latest annual report to the Welsh Language Board recorded good progress in the development of our Welsh language services, through the attainment of National Vocational Qualifications in Business Welsh, by staff based in HSE's office in Wales. We have also continued to expand our range of publications in Welsh, including formal reports on incidents.

Private finance initiative (PFI)

1.187   The Health and Safety Laboratory (an agency of HSE) continues to make progress towards the rationalisation of its estate to better meet its future needs. A preferred bidder has been chosen for a PFI option and the proposal is to build a new laboratory on the Buxton site. A ministerial decision on the project is due in early 2000 with an occupation date by mid-2002.

1.188   Consultants have completed a feasibility study of short-listed proposals for the rationalisation of the HSE Merseyside HQ estate. Funding options, including those under the PFI, are being explored.

Prompt payment of bills

1.189   HSE's combined prompt payment performance (HSE and HSL) for 1998/99 is 94.1% of supplier bills paid on time. Although an improvement in performance this fell short of the Government target of paying 97.5% of bills on time.

1.190   HSE's performance improved this year as a result of implementing the findings of a compliance audit with BS 7980 (British Standard for Achieving Good Payment Performance in Commercial Transactions) and developing more sophisticated analysis and reporting tools, which became available from January 1999.

Quinquennial review

1.191   Work has proceeded during the year to pursue the recommendations of the Quinquennial review of HSC/E which reported early in 1998. In particular:

- HSC examined options to extend charging and concluded it was feasible to charge for safety case assessment and related inspection in the gas, offshore and railway industries and installations subject to the Control of Major Accident Hazards Regulations (COMAH);

- HELA undertook research to build on existing activity to identify and spread best practice on consistency of enforcement among local authorities. HELA will publish the results during 1999 and has identified priorities for further action; and

- The revision of the Framework of Accountabilities document which sets out the relationship between HSC/E, DETR and other government departments is almost complete.

Charging

1.192   The Ministerial decision that charging should be extended was received in early November 1998, as part of the Comprehensive Spending Review settlement. We consulted on the proposals for the administrative and financial arrangements for the COMAH charging regime. The COMAH Regulations 1999 included regulations enabling HSE to charge for its functions as part of the competent authority.

1.193   In the meantime, draft regulatory proposals for the gas transportation, offshore and rail industry charging regimes have been developed and a consultation exercise will be conducted during late April to early July 1999. It is intended that the Regulations enabling HSE to charge for the assessment of safety cases, granting approvals and regulatory activities to ensure compliance with the safety case in these industries will come into force from October 1999.

Resource accounting and budgeting

1.194   Resource accounting and budgeting (RAB) is expected to be fully operational from 1 April 2001 and is the application of accruals accounting techniques to income and expenditure. It governs how items are to be reported, with an analysis against aims and their supporting objectives. It also extends to all aspects of planning, controlling and in-year monitoring.

1.195   We are on course to meet the trigger points strategy recently introduced with Parliamentary agreement to monitor progress on the implementation of RAB within government departments. We are publishing an audited set of resource accounts as an appendix to HSC/E's Annual Accounts for 1998/99 (Section 2).

1.196   Work on resource budgeting continues and we are participating in further tests as directed by HM Treasury in drawing up preliminary resource-based estimates for 2000/01.

Use of consultants

1.197   HSE continued to exercise systems of control over the procurement, appointment and use of consultancy services to ensure that they provide value for money and a worthwhile enhancement to HSE's activities. Such systems included:

- the provision of advice by the procurement support unit to ensure compliance with policies on the use of consultants;

- scrutiny of specifications to ensure that requirements are properly defined;

- the appointment of a nominated project officer with authority to manage and to be held accountable for each project; and

- the use of a proper business case to establish the purpose and benefits of each project.

Devolution

1.198   Health and safety at work matters have not been devolved to Scotland's Parliament, or to the National Assembly for Wales. Separate arrangements for health and safety which already existed in Northern Ireland have been largely unaffected by devolution. HSC/E's activities will be of continuing interest to the newly elected Members in Scotland and Wales and HSE officials have been working closely with their colleagues in Scotland and Wales during 1998/99 to set out arrangements for continued effective liaison.

Internal Year 2000 issues

1.199   HSE has been working since 1996 to ensure that its IT systems will not be affected by the Millennium Bug. All IT systems have been tested; some have been replaced and others are being fixed. Based on the work and testing carried out by HSE staff (with external support) it is believed that all IT systems will be Year 2000 compliant before November 1999.

1.200   In addition, HSE has conducted impact tests, where several IT systems have been run concurrently to see how they impact on each other. These tests also suggest that HSE's IT systems should work effectively together.

1.201   Attention has been given to HSE's business continuity plan which addresses the business-critical non-IT systems for HSE. This includes: planned availability of IT systems, including telephones; access to buildings and building services; emergency support to industry, including emergency rooms; duty officer system; work of the Secretariat and Press Office staff to inform Ministers, the Commission and the Board of developments during the Millennium; personnel issues; and issues for the leap year date in February/March 2000.

ANNEXES

OUTPUT AND PERFORMANCE ANALYSIS

CONTEXTUAL INDICATORS (the environment in which HSE carries out its mission and aims)

HSE's mission: to ensure that risks to people's health and safety from work activities are properly controlled.		
Fatal and major injury rate for workers, per 100 000	128.5, 97/98 (final rate) 119.0, 98/99 (estimated final rate)	Change in RIDDOR means more reported injuries are classified as major injuries therefore rates higher. Source: *'The costs to Britain of workplace accidents and work-related ill health in 1995/96'* HSE Books 1999 ISBN 0 7176 1709 2.
Estimated cost to society of work accidents and work-related ill health.	£14.5 - £18.1 billion* (1995/96 prices)	
- of which cost of work-related ill health.	£10.2 - £10.6 billion** (1995/96 prices)	

OUTPUT MEASURES (how HSE carries out its aims)

	1997/98 Outturn	1998/99 Plan	1998/99 **Outturn**	*NOTES*
Aim 1: Modernise and simplify legal framework, by:				
Introducing: sets of regulations, approved codes of practice, consultative documents and new guidance documents	56	70	**66**	Indicator of one aspect of this work. Many policy outputs difficult to forecast. Some policy products did not materialise for reasons outside HSE's control. We also had to deal with some unplanned work.
Aim 2: Secure compliance with the law, by:				
Making regulatory contacts, including inspections and investigations, with employers and duty holders	186 065	170 000	**183 292**	Includes all operational site visits, office meetings etc with 'clients'. Includes the results of inspection campaigns in the agriculture, construction and manufacturing sectors.

	1997/98 Outturn	1998/99 Plan	1998/99 **Outturn**	*Notes*
Investigating incidents/complaints	33 585	29 000	**32 270**	Cases completed, some of which may involve more than one contact.
Considering and processing safety cases/reports and nuclear licence actions	658	740	**759**	Demand-led measure, beyond HSE's control. Includes: offshore safety cases, onshore major hazard safety reports and nuclear licence actions.
Aim 3: Provide information and advice, by:				
Dealing with enquiries	448 000	550 000	**476 499**	Largely a demand-led measure.
Making available a range of publicity products	2 707	2 100	**4 489**	Includes: publications, titles, exhibitions/displays, press adverts, notices and briefings, internet pages, video titles, Autofax titles. Outturn reflects the continuing popularity of (and HSE's work on) electronic media.
Number of publicity products purchased or accessed, millions	7.4	7.7	**11.6**	Includes: free leaflets issued, publications sold, videos hired/sold, accesses to Autofax, internet 'hits'. Noticeable shift in emphasis from printed to electronic media.
Aim 4: Promote risk assessment and technological understanding, by:				
Letting research contracts	340	300	**309**	
Implementing risk and technical policy projects (some of these contribute to other aims)		120	**126**	New measure, reflecting HSE's expertise in applying risk concepts, science and technology to help produce policy and field outputs.
Aim 5: Operate statutory schemes, by:				
Providing regulatory services, eg issuing statutory certificates	4 218	3 600	**3 834**	This is an aggregate measure - see page 53 for list of service items included.

PERFORMANCE MEASURES (efficiency and quality aspects of how HSE carries out its aims)

	1997/98 OUTTURN	1998/99 PLAN	1998/99 OUTTURN	*NOTES*
Aim 1: Modernise & simplify legal framework				
% sets of regulations, approved codes of practice, consultative documents & guidance documents introduced to time	84	88	82	Slight fall in this quality measure, due mainly to factors outside HSE's control e.g implementation of some regulations delayed to allow for more consultation.
Aim 2: Secure compliance with the law				
% high hazard/risk workplaces receiving annual regulatory contact	100	100	96	Slight shortfall due partly to inspectors judging that some of these sites were misclassified and did not need inspecting.
% complaints (about work activities) investigated	74	85	77	Higher than expected number of complaints received resulting in lower proportion investigated.
% reported events (accidents/incidents) investigated	6.9	6.1	5.7	HSE is seeking to improve this aspect of performance. Next year's target is higher at 6.7% (See paragraph 1.123).
% safety cases/reports and nuclear licence actions processed to time	90	87	89	
% prosecutions resulting in convictions	79	targets not set	83[P]	
% inspector time on site/contact and related activities (as a proportion of total time available)	79	80	78	Slight fall in this quality measure. Explanation given in paragraph 1.129.
Aim 3: Provide information and advice				
% public enquiries answered within 10 days	97	100	97	Continuing Citizen's Charter commitment[††].
% customer satisfaction with HSE service[+]	86	targets not set	79	Citizen's Charter measure (see general note below).

	1997/98 OUTTURN	1998/99 PLAN	1998/99 OUTTURN	NOTES
Number of justified or partly justified complaints against HSE staff per 100,000 contacts	6	targets not set	5	Citizen's Charter measure. Contacts include all public enquiries plus regulatory contacts (see general note below).
Aim 4: Promote risk assessment and technological understanding				
% research projects completed to time	95	95	95	This measure is to be discontinued and replaced by a more meaningful one.
% risk and technical policy projects completed to time		70	79	New measure.
Aim 5: Operate statutory schemes				
% service products (statutory certificates etc) processed to time	90	88	94	Excludes mines approvals and exemptions.
Aim 6: Ensure efficient central services[†]				
Efficiency gains (cash and productivity) as % of total running costs	5.3	4	3	Further details of our efficiency programme are given on pages 57-58.
Staff costs (as % total) devoted to central services (personnel, planning, finance etc)	8.2	7.9	8.1	The size of HSE's 'overhead' is set to reduce further over the next 3 years, reflecting improved efficiency.

Notes:

HSE does not set targets for certain measures and indicators i.e. prosecution conviction rates, some Citizens' Charter results, measures that are demand led and measures that are beyond our control. Instead, where necessary, the term 'expected demand level' is used.

[+] *Customer satisfaction with main regulatory interface is measured by a 2 year rolling survey across HSE's 7 FOD regions (4 were surveyed in 1997/98 and 3 in 1998/99). On average over the 2 years 82% indicated they were satisfied with the service they received. One region was significantly below the average and the reasons for this are being investigated.*

[†] *Aim 6 now considered an internal business aim.*

[††] *Citizen's Charter was replaced by Service First in June 1998.*

P *Provisional.*

[*] *These costs include the net present value of costs in future years. Costs incurred in 1995/96 are £9.9 - £14.1 billion.*

[**] *These costs include the net present values of costs in future years. Costs incurred in 1995/96 are £6.2 - £7.2 billion.*

LEGISLATIVE PROJECTS

Work started or completed during the year

Projects started   (a)   **International**

Dangerous Substances (Marketing and Use) Regulations
Health and Safety **(Miscellaneous Modifications)**
Regulations

Ionising Radiations Regulations
Radiation (Emergency Preparedness and Public Information) Regulations

Nuclear Reactors (Assessment of Environmental Effects of Decommissioning) Regulations

Chemicals (Hazard Information and Packaging for Supply) (Amendment) (no 2) Regulations

       (b)   **Domestic**

Manufacture and **Storage of Explosives** Regulations
Dangerous Substances in Harbour Areas Regulations
Fire Certificates (Special Premises) Regulations
Revised ACoP on **Lift Truck Operator Training**
Control of **Ground Movement in Mines** Regulations and ACoP

Electricity in Mines Regulations and revised ACoP
Underground Transport in Mines Regulations and ACoP
Respirable Dust in Coal Mines
Use of Explosives in Non-Safety Lamp Mines
Railway Safety Regulations
Petroleum Safety Regulations
Health and Safety **(Investigations of Accidents)** Regulations
Pipeline Safety Regulations
Shipment of Radioactive Substances (Enforcement) Regulations
Revision of **Gas Safety Management** Regulations

Consultative/Discussion documents published	**(a)**	**International**
		Asbestos (Prohibitions) Regulations **Asbestos** (Management of Risk in Workplace Premises) Regulations
		Asbestos (Tightening Licensing and Control Measures) Regulations
		Contained Use of Genetically Modified Micro-organisms **Biocidal Products** Health and Safety **(Miscellaneous Modifications)** Regulations
	(b)	**Domestic**
		Substances that cause **Occupational Asthma** **First-aid Offshore** revised ACoP Managing **Stress at Work** Control of **Legionellosis** Consolidation of **Health and Safety at Quarries** Regulations
Projects completed	**(a)**	**International**
		Control of Lead at Work (Amendment) Regulations **Transport of Dangerous Goods** (Safety Advisers) Regulations 1999
		The **Carriage of Dangerous Goods** (Amendment) Regulations 1999
		The **Control of Major Accident Hazards** Regulations 1999
		Police (Health and Safety) Regulations 1999 **Provision and Use of Work Equipment** Regulations 1998 **Lifting Operations and Lifting Equipment** Regulations 1998
		Genetically Modified Organisms (Contained Use) (Amendment) Regulations 1998

(b)   Domestic

The Prevention of **Accidents to Children in Agriculture**
Regulations 1998

Control of Substances Hazardous to Health Regulations
1999

Police Diving ACoP
Revised **Gas Safety** (Installation and Use) Regulations 1998
Health and Safety (Fees) Regulations 1999
Control of **Asbestos** at Work (Amendment) Regulations
1998

Health and Safety **(Enforcing Authority)** Regulations

EUROPEAN UNION LEGISLATIVE ACTIVITY

Proposals published by the EC during period 1 April 1998 - 31 March 1999

Directive/Instrument	Date published	Lead department
Dangerous Substances Classification, Packaging and Labelling 24th Adaptation	April 1998	HSE
Gassy Mines Directive	March 1998	HSE
Dangerous Substances Classification 25th Adaptation	November 1998	HSE
Workers in potentially explosive atmospheres	July 1998	HSE
Scaffolding	December 1998	HSE

Directives progressed, or where common position or adoption was recorded during period 1 April 1998 - 31 March 1999

EC Number	Directive	Position	Lead dept
Not yet issued	**New Directive on Chemical Preparations**	Reached common position 25/09/98	HSE
Not yet issued	**Workers in potentially explosive atmospheres**	Reached common position 22/12/98	HSE
Not yet issued	**Carcinogens 2nd Amendment**	Reached common position 22/12/98	HSE
Not yet issued	**Dangerous Goods Safety Adviser Sibling Directive**	Reached common position 29/03/99	DETR
Not yet issued	**Transportable Pressure Equipment**	Reached common position 30/11/98	DETR
98/8/EC	**Biocides**	Adopted 24/04/98	HSE
98/73/EC	**Dangerous Substances Classification, Packaging and Labelling 24th Adaptation**	Adopted 18/09/98	HSE
98/65/EC	**Gassy Mines Directive**	Adopted 03/09/98	HSE
98/98/EC	**Dangerous Substances Classification, Packaging and Labelling 25th Adaptation**	Adopted 15/12/98	HSE
98/24/EC	**Chemical Agents**	Adopted 07/04/98	HSE
98/81/EC	**Genetically Modified Micro Organisms, Contained Use of, Amendment**	Adopted 26/10/98	HSE
98/30/EC	**Gas Liberalisation**	Adopted 22/06/98	DTI
99/43/EC	**Marketing and Use Directive, 17th Amendment**	Adopted 31/12/98	DTI

SELECTED HSE PUBLICATIONS

Annual reports/information

HELA: Annual report 1999 MISC 182 1999 (free)

HELA: National picture of health and safety in the local authority enforced sectors 1999
MISC 182 1999 (free)

HSC Strategic plan for 1999/2000 1999 ISBN 0 7176 2438 2

HSC Health and safety statistics 1997/98 1998 ISBN 0 7176 1636 3

Railway safety: HM Chief Inspector of Railways Annual Report on the safety record of the railways in Great Britain during 1997/98 1998 ISBN 07176 1655 X

Selected titles

Application of electro-sensitive protective equipment using light curtains and light beam devices in machinery HSG180 1999 ISBN 0 7176 1550 2

Approved supply list (Supplement to the 4th edition) 1999 ISBN 0 7176 1683 5

Are you involved in a diving project? INDG266 1998 (free)

Assessment principles for offshore safety cases HSG181 1998 ISBN 0 7176 1238 4

The bulk transfer of dangerous liquids and gases between ship and shore HSG186 1999
ISBN 0 7176 1644 4

CHIP Approved supply list (4th edition) L115 1998 ISBN 0 7176 1641 X

Commercial diving projects inland/inshore - Approved Code of Practice L104 1998
ISBN 0 7176 1495 6

Contingency planning for a safe year 2000 INDG283 1998 (free)

The control of asbestos at work   Approved Code of Practice (2nd edition) L27 1999
ISBN 0 7176 1673 8

Control of diesel engine exhaust emissions in the workplace HSG187 1999
ISBN 0 7176 1662 2

Controlled asbestos stripping techniques for work requiring a licence HSG189/1 1999
ISBN 0 7176 1666 5

Ear protection: Employers' duties explained INDG298 1999 (free)

Five steps to risk assessment: Case studies 1998 HSG183 ISBN 0 7176 1580 4

Guidance on the handling, storage and transport of airbags and seat belt pretensioners HSG184 1998 ISBN 0 7176 1598 7

Guidance on the Noise at Work Regulations 1989 L108 1998 0 7176 1511 1

A guide to the Offshore Installations (Safety Representatives and Safety Committees) Regulations 1989 (revised) L110 1998 ISBN 0 7176 1549 9

Health and safety and the Year 2000 problem INDG267 1998 (free)

Health and safety at motor sports events: A guide for employers and organisers 1999 HSG112 ISBN 0 7176 0705 4

Health and safety in excavations: Be safe and shore HSG185 1999 ISBN 0 7176 1563 4

Health risk from hand-arm vibration: Advice for employers and the self employed INDG126 (rev 1) 1998 (free)

Health risk management: A guide to working with solvents HSG188 1999 ISBN 0 7176 1664 9

Help on work-related stress INDG281 1998 (free)

HSC policy statement on open government INDG179 (revised) 1998 (free)

Keep your top on INDG147 (rev 1) 1998 (free)

Landlords: A guide to landlords' duties: Gas Safety (Installation and Use) Regulations 1998 INDG285 1999 (free)

Major hazard sites and the millennium problem 1998 ISBN 0 7176 1639 8

Managing confined spaces on farms AIS26 1998 (free)

Managing health and safety: Five steps to success INDG275 1998 (free)

Manual handling L23 (2nd edition) 1998 ISBN 0 7176 2415 3

Occupational exposure limits EH40 1999 ISBN 0 7176 1660 6

Offshore health and safety legislation: Your questions answered INDG274 1998 (free)

Protect your hearing (pocket card) INDG299 1999 (free)

Railway accident at Watford 1999 ISBN 0 7176 1510 3

Railway accident at Bexley 1999 ISBN 0 7176 1658 4

Safe use of vehicles on construction sites HSG144 1998 ISBN 0 7176 1610 X

Safeguarding agricultural machinery HSG89 1998 (revised) ISBN 0 7176 2400 5

Safety and the Year 2000 1998 ISBN 0 7176 1491 3

Safety in the installation and use of gas systems and appliances Approved Code of Practice L56 1998 ISBN 0 7176 1635 5

Safety representatives and safety committees on offshore installations INDG119 (rev 1) 1999

Scientific and archaeological diving projects Approved Code of Practice L107 1998
ISBN 0 7176 1498 0

Short guide to the Employers Liabilty (Compulsory Insurance) Act 1969: A guide for employers HSE4 (revised) 1998 (free)

Sound Solutions Offshore: Practical examples of noise reduction HSG182 1998 ISBN 0 7176 1581 2

Summary criteria for occupational exposure limits -1998 supplement EH64 1998
ISBN 0 7176 1576 6

Testing safety-related control systems for Year 2000 compliance 1998 ISBN 0 7176 1596 0

Veterinary medicines: Safe use by farmers and other animal handlers AS31 1998 (free)

Wear ear protection correctly MISC185 1999 (free)

Work with asbestos insulation, asbestos coating and asbestos insulating board - Approved Code of Practice (2nd edition) L28 1999 ISBN 0 7176 1674 6

Working with asbestos cement HSG189/2 1999 ISBN 0 7176 1667 3

Working with VDUs INDG36 (rev 1) 1998 (free)

Year 2000 risk assessment: Will you come through the millenium safely? INDG287
1999 (free)

Multimedia products

Approved carriage list CD ROM (revised) 1999 (a step by step guide to inspection of vehicles containing dangerous substances carried by road) ISBN 0 7176 1685 1

Bookfinder CD ROM 1998 (this is an electronic catalogue of HSE publications)

Carriage of dangerous goods by road CD ROM 1998 (this CD ROM package is aimed at all those involved in the carriage of dangerous goods by road and those who enforce the regulations) ISBN 0 7176 1572 3

Essentials routemap 1999 (this software takes you through a series of questions to help you check the state of your business in health and safety terms) ISBN 0 7176 2416 1

Videos

Best signs story 1998 UK 4405

Cutting edge II - a series of three videos promoting the management of health and safety in the woodworking industry

Part 1 - managing for safety 1998 UK 4414

Part 2 - a safe machine 1998 UK4412

Part 3 - a healthy business 1998 UK 4413

Don't fall for it 1999 UK 4424

Escaping the maze...of health and safety information 1998 UK 4404

Fatal traction 1998 UK 4409

Hard to handle 1998 UK 4407

High designs 1998 UK 4402

Safe tractor driving on slopes 1999 UK 4425

Safe use of printing chemicals: COSHH and substitution 1998 UK 4406

HSE videos are available from:

HSE videos, Dept VC
PO Box 35
Wetherby
West Yorkshire
LS23 7EX

Tel: 0845 741 9411 (all calls charged at local rate)
Fax: 01937 541083
e-mail: euroview@compuserve.com
http://www.euroview.co.uk

STATISTICS ON ENFORCEMENT ACTION AND PENALTIES

The following table summarises HSE's enforcement activity since 1987/88. More information, including the work of local authorities, can be found in HSC's *Health and safety statistics*.

HSE inspectors decide what enforcement action to take in particular cases in accordance with the HSC's published Enforcement Policy Statement. The provisional figures for 1998/99 indicate that HSE issued 10 844 enforcement notices. This is over 20% higher than the previous year, entirely the result of more improvement notices being issued.

The provisional figures also indicate that, in 1998/99, prosecutions were brought for 1 797 health and safety offences in 1 058 separate cases. Slightly over 83% of offences prosecuted resulted in conviction.

The average fine for 1998/99 based on provisional figures for the whole of HSE was £5 038. The majority of HSE prosecutions are brought by its Field Operations Directorate which spent a total of 112 inspector years on formal enforcement work in 1998/99.

The types of enforcement action referred to in the tables are defined as follows:

Improvement notices require employers to take remedial action on specific breaches of the law within a specified time limit;

Prohibition notices are issued in cases where the inspector believes that a work activity involves or will involve a risk of serious personal injury. Prohibition notices can take two forms:

- **immediate prohibition notices** which stop a work activity immediately until a risk is dealt with; and

- **deferred prohibition notices** which stop a work activity within a specified time limit, for example, because the risk of injury does not require immediate action to control it, or where it would be unwise to interrupt a process in mid-cycle.

Crown bodies are bound by the requirements of health and safety legislation but are not subject to statutory enforcement notices or prosecution. Non-statutory procedures are in place for the issue of Crown improvement and prohibition notices, and for the censure of Crown bodies in circumstances in which a prosecution would otherwise have been brought. In 1998/99, HSE issued a total of 14 Crown enforcement notices: 13 improvement notices; and one immediate prohibition notice. HSE censured four Crown bodies. (These figures are not included in the table opposite).

ENFORCEMENT ACTION, PROSECUTIONS AND NOTICES ISSUED BY HSE 1987/88-1998/99p

Prosecutions				
	Duty-holders prosecuted (a)	Total offences prosecuted (b)(c)	Of which, offences leading to conviction	Average penalty per conviction (d)
1987/88 (e)	1350	2337	2053	792 (f)
1988/89	1409	2328	2090	541
1989/90	1557	2653	2289	783 (g)
1990/91	1397	2312	1991	903 (h)
1991/92	1425	2424	2126	1181 (i)
1992/93	1324	2157	1865	1390
1993/94	1156	1793	1507	3103 (j)
1994/95	1111	1803	1499	2873 (k)
1995/96	1087	1767	1451	2572
1996/97	861	1490	1195	5274 (l)
1997/98	935	1627	1284	4694 (m)
1998/99p	1058	1797	1493	5038 (n)
Notices issued by type				
	Improvement	Deferred prohibition	Immediate prohibition	Total notices
1987/88	6631	234	4296	11 161
1988/89	6693	189	4664	11 546
1989/90	7610	200	4332	12 142
1990/91	8489	227	4022	12 738
1991/92	8395	222	3802	12 419
1992/93	7462	201	4251	11 914
1993/94	6484	144	3961	10 589
1994/95	6512	124	4172	10 808
1995/96	5219	82	3385	8 686
1996/97	3770	165	3509	7 444
1997/98	4411	181	4319	8 911
1998/99p	6328	198	4318	10 844

Notes:

(a)   *This figure may include certain employers or other duty-holders who have been prosecuted on more than one occasion. Each prosecution may concern more than one offence.*

(b)   *Each offence prosecuted represents one information laid or, in Scotland, individual charges.*

(c)   *Includes, for Scotland, individual charges.*

(d)   *Figures for average penalty are actuals.*

(e)   *Years commencing 1 April.*

(f)   *Includes fines totalling £750 000 imposed against a petroleum company. If these convictions are excluded the average fine for 1987/88 was £427.*

(g)   *Includes one fine of £100 000. If this conviction is excluded the average fine for 1989/90 was £739.*

(h)   *Includes two separate fines of £250 000 and £100 000 (reduced from £250 000 on appeal in November 1990). If these convictions are excluded the average fine for 1990/91 was £728.*

(i)   *Includes three separate fines of £250 000 and £100 000 against individual corporations. If these convictions are excluded the average fine for 1991/92 was £970.*

(j)   *Includes three individual fines of £250 000 and single fines of £150 000 and £100 000. The average fine for 1993/94 without these convictions was £2447.*

(k)   *Includes two individual fines of £200 000 and £100 000. If these convictions are excluded the average fine for 1994/95 was £2677.*

(l)   *Includes four separate fines of £750 000, £500 000, £250 000 and £125 000, fines totalling £400 000 against one company and six individual fines of £100 000. If these convictions are excluded the average fine for 1996/97 was £3113.*

(m)   *Includes four separate fines of £150 000, one for £175 000 and four of £100 000. If these convictions are excluded the average fine for 1997/98 was £3805.*

(n)   *Includes one fine of £1 200 000, two for £500 000 and two of £100 000. If these convictions are excluded the average fine for 1998/99p was £3442.*

(p)   *provisional.*

HSC ADVISORY COMMITTEES

The Health and Safety Commission has 14 Industry Advisory Committees and seven Subject Advisory Committees as listed below:

Industry Advisory Committees

- Adventure activities
- Agriculture
- Ceramic
- Construction
- Deep mined coal
- Education services
- Foundries
- Health services
- Oil
- Paper and Board
- Printing
- Railways
- Rubber
- Textiles

Subject Advisory Committees

- Dangerous pathogens
- Dangerous substances
- Genetic modification
- Ionising radiations
- Occupational health
- Safety of nuclear installations
- Toxic substances

All the committees produce and publish guidance with the Commission's endorsement. Subject Advisory Committees allow the Commission to take views on difficult issues, typically of cross-departmental interest. They provide formal consultation mechanisms in areas of high public and political sensitivity, such as genetic modification; and the involvement of outside experts helps give legitimacy to their, and to the Commission's activities. They also act as a sounding-board for HSE proposals.

HSC's Advisory Committees encourage the joint participation of all representative organisations in the improvement of health and safety at work; draw on the expertise and advice available on both sides of industry and elsewhere; give the problems of particular industries closer and more detailed attention then the Commission itself is able to do; and allow an industry focus on general issues (such as noise and COSHH).

HSC also takes advice from the Health and Safety Executive/Local Authorities Enforcement Liaison Committee (HELA), which seeks to ensure consistency among local authorities and HSE.

Members of HSC Advisory Committees

Members of HSC's Advisory Committees as at 31 March 1999

Industry Advisory Committees

Adventure activities: Mrs Jane Willis **(Chair)**; Mr John Bevan; Ms Dorothy Breckenbridge; Mr Chris Coleman; Mr Brian Davis; Mr Jim Hammett; Mr Rob Henderson; Mr Martin Hudson; Ms Pat Mee; Mr Drew Michie; Mr Fred Nelson; Mr Iain Peter; Mr Robert Phillips; Mr Ron Rutland; Mr Stephen Saddler; Ms Carol Sherriff.

Agriculture: Mr David Mattey **(Chair)**; Mr Brian Collen; Mr Marcus Themans; Mr Barrie Hudson; Mr David Swaffer; Mr Russell Evans; Mr John Littlefair; Mr Barry Leathwood; Mr Ivan Monckton; Mr Stuart Neale; Mr Peter Kirkby; Mr Peter Dracup; Ms Teresa Mackay.

Ceramics: Mr Ed Friend **(Chair)**; Mr Francis Morrall; Mr Keith Morton; Mr Dennis Beattie; Mr Stuart Adams; Dr Malcolm Moore; Mr Harry Fraser; Mr Mick Young; Mr Roger Pearman; Mr Garry Oakes; Mr John Alcock; Mr Len McCluskey; Mr Nigel Bryson.

Construction: Mrs Sandra Caldwell **(Chair)**; Mr Mike Totterdell MBE; Mr Chris McEwen; Mr Tom Gallagher; Mr Andy Lewis; Mr John Varcoe; Mr Peter Bray; Mr Tony Wheel; Mr Nigel Bryson; Mr Ivan Moldawczuk; Mr Bob Blackman; Mr Alan Ritchie; Mr Malcolm Bonnett; Mr Fred Pound; Mr Robin Powell; Mr Sydney Bell; Mr Brian Mansell OBE; Mr Paul Everall; Mr Dermot Breen; Mr Tom Mellish; Miss Suzannah Thursfield; Mr Jim Murray.

Deep mined coal: Mr Brian Langdon CBE **(Chair)**; Mr Ramsay Dow; Mr Alec Galloway; Mr Jim Sorbie; Mr Geoff Underwood; Mr David Flack; Mr Neil Greatrex; Mr Ross Letham; Mr Bob Young.

Education services: Mr John Cullen **(Chair)**; Mrs Gillian Ross-Pond; Mr Peter Humphreys; Mr Robert Hellings; Mr Roy Atkinson; Miss Gale Waller; Mr Christopher Storr; Mr Michael Sant; Ms Daphne Griffith; Mr Fred Sherwood; Mr Ken WImbor; Mr Andrew Morris; Mr David Kempson; Mr Ian Draper; Mr Phil Barley; Mr Peter Hart; Mr Steve Craig; Ms Hope Daley; Ms Erica Halvorsen; Mr Sharon Liburd; Mr Robert Ashworth; Mr Chris Purser.

Foundries: Mr Ed Friend **(Chair)**; Mr Trevor Askey; Dr Jim Birch; Mr Alan Harvey; Mr Alf Lloyd; Mr Tony McCarthy; Dr Glyn Morley; Mr Richard O'Sullivan; Mr Tim Parker; Mr Alan Robson; Mr Martin Shenton; Mr Roger Turley MBE.

Health services: Mr John Cullen **(Chair)**; Mr Brain Gibbs; Mrs Irene Longstaff; Mr Martin Gower; Mr Julian Coulden; Mr Francis Ursell; Ms Maggie Marum; Mr John Rostil; Mr John Hunt; Mr Tony Wells; Ms Wilma MacPherson; Dr Robert Davies; Mr Philip Green; Ms Kim Sunley; Mr Jon Richards; Ms Claire Sullivan; Mr Mick Balfour; Ms Sheelagh Brewer; Ms Eleanor Ransom; Mr Mike Chapman; Mrs Carol Dolbear; Dr Janet Carruthers; Mr Tom Mellish.

Oil: Mr Clive Norris **(Chair)**; Mr John Frew; Mr David Henson; Dr Jim Keech; Mr Philip Ley; Mr Ian McCulloch; Mr Ian McPherson; Mr Clive Sheil; Mr Paul Wood; Mr Laurence Attwood; Mr Robert Buirds; Mr Campbell Reid MBE; Mr Roger Spiller; Mr John Taylor; Mr Steve Todd; Mr Rab Wilson; Mr Ron Wood.

Paper and board: Mr Andrew Porter **(Chair)**; Mr Jim Reeves; Mr Duncan Simpson; Mr Adrian Cunningham; Mr Michael Eede; Mr Bud Hudspith; Mr George Beattie; Mr David Gillett; Mr Colin Scott; Mr Peter McLaverty; Mr Colin Britchford; Mr Alistair Smith.

Printing: Mr Andrew Porter **(Chair)**; Mr Tim Gopsill; Mr Dick Barker; Mr Bud Hudspith; Mr Denis Spencer; Mr Peter Taylor; Mr Ian Wilcock; Mr John Fuller; Mr Walter Stothard; Mr David Barker; Mr Graham Cooper; Mr Brian Purkiss; Mr Peter Yapp; Mr Mike Griffiths; Mr Andy Metcalf.

Railways: Mr Vic Coleman **(Chair)**; Mr Graham Brown; Mr Jeremy Cranfield; Mr Paul Godier;

Mr Paul Abbott; Mr Aidan Nelson; Mr Dennis Cameron; Mr Bob Shannon; Mr Vernon Hince; Mr William MacKenzie; Mr John Cartledge; Mr David Heseldine.

Rubber: Mr Andrew Porter **(Chair)**; Mr Martin Smith; Mr David Simpson; Dr Ken Straughan; Ms Sheila Ikin; Mr Ian Smith; Mr John Redmond; Mr David Sheddon; Mr Albert Smith; Mr Bill Holmes; Mr Gary McKittrick; Mr Duncan Simpson; Ms Margaret Armstrong; Mr Thomas Picken; Mr John Hann; Mr Jim Marshall; Mr Kevin O'Reilly.

Textiles: Mr Andrew Porter **(Chair)**; Mr Paul Gates; Mr Des Ferrell; Mr Peter Booth; Mrs Sheila Bearcroft; Mr Jack Firth; Mr John Rutherford; Mr Gordon Rudd; Mr Phillip Mitchell; Mr Tom Ashdown; Ms Anne Carvell; Mr Andrew Wolmersley; Mr David Duckworth; Mr Allen Jones.

Subject Advisory Committees

Dangerous pathogens: Professor Roger Whittenbury **(Chair)**; Dr Barbara Bannister; Professor Roger Freeman; Dr Ernie Gould; Professor Don Jeffries; Mr Martin Jones; Dr Phil Jones; Professor Catherine Peckham;Professor Brian Spratt; Mr Bob Clare; Ms Anne Harris; Professor Charles Hart; Mr John Saxby; Ms Janet MacCullogh; Dr Ron Owen; Ms Pam Smith; Mr Paul Taylor.

Dangerous substances: Mr Clive Norris **(Chair)**; Dr Chris Beaton; Mr Robin Marshall; Dr Roger Pullen; Mr Dave Matthews; Mr Tom Mellish; Dr Tony Cox; Dr Mike Hogh; Professor Philip Nolan; Mr Brian Hazell; Mr Bernie Cahill.

Genetic modification: Professor Kay Davies CBE **(Chair)**; Professor John Beringer CBE; Mrs Dot Carey; Dr Kenneth Edwards; Professor Mike Gale; Professor Steven Hughes; Dr Julian Kindlerer; Dr Ron Owen OBE; Professor Mike Roberts; Mr Roger Spiller; Mr Stephen Vranch.

Ionising radiations: Dr Sam Harbison CB **(Chair)**; Dr Penny Allisy-Roberts OBE; Professor Keith Boddy CBE; Professor Roger Clarke; Dr Roger Coates; Dr Wynne Davies; Mr Steve Ebdon-Jackson; Mr John Godfrey; Dr Keith Harding; Mr John Kane; Miss Margaret Minski; Mr Roger Moore; Dr Hamish Porter; Mr David Robinson; Mr Bill Ross CBE; Mr David Small; Mr Mike Smallwood; Dr Dick Taylor; Dr Janet Turp.

Occupational health: Dr Peter Graham **(Chair)**; Dr Sue Robson; Dr Sally Dymott MBE; Dr Ken Prudhoe; Mr Alan Lloyd; Mr Doug Russell; Dr Patrick Flippance; Dr Derek White; Mr Graeme Pykett; Ms Kim Sunley; Mr Stephen Bailey; Dr Ron Owen OBE.

Safety of nuclear installations: Sir David Harrison **(Chair)**; Mr Gordon Bellard; Professor David Blockley; Professor Sue Cox; Dr Wynne Davies; Professor Keith Duncan; Professor Tony Goddard; Professor John Head; Dr Bob Hall; Mr John Hall; Professor John Knott; Professor Bev Littlewood; Dr Rod Mckenzie; Mr Stephen Napier; Professor David Owens; Dr Susan Parry; Professor Neville Moray; Dr Jim Whiston.

Toxic substances: Dr Peter Graham **(Chair)**; Dr Janet Asherson; Dr Steve Bailey; Dr Alan Bell; Dr Ian Carney;Professor Nicola Cherry; Mr Christopher Fry; Dr Alastair Hay; Ms Elizabeth Jenkins; Dr Michael Kingsland;Dr Leonard Levy; Ms Gwynne Lyons; Mr Graham Philbin; Dr Christopher Soutar; Dr Andrew Stirling; Mr Owen Tudor; Mr Harry Wilson.

REGIONAL OFFICES

Region	Address and local authorities covered within each region

Wales and West

Government Buildings, Ty Glas, Llanishen, Cardiff CF4 5SH. Tel: 01222 263000
The Region comprises the Unitary Councils of Wales, North Somerset, Bath and North East Somerset, Bristol City, South Gloucestershire, Plymouth City, Torbay, Herefordshire, Telford and Wrekin and the Counties of Somerset, Cornwall, Devon, Gloucestershire, Worcestershire, Shropshire and Staffordshire.

Home Counties

14 Cardiff Road, Luton, Bedfordshire, LU1 1PP. Tel: 0158 444200
The Region comprises the Unitary Councils of Bournemouth, Brighton and Hove, Luton, Milton Keynes, Isle of Wight, Poole, Portsmouth City, Southampton City, Swindon, Peterborough City, Bracknell Forest, Reading, Slough, Southend-on-Sea, Thurrock, West Berkshire, Royal Windsor and Maidenhead, Wokingham and the Counties of Bedfordshire, Buckinghamshire, Cambridgeshire, Dorset, Essex, Hampshire, Hertfordshire, Norfolk, Suffolk and Wiltshire.

London and South East

St Dunstans House, 201-211 Borough High Street, SE1 1GZ. Tel: 0171 556 2100
The Region comprises the Unitary Council of Medway and the Counties of Kent, Surrey, East Sussex, West Sussex and all the London Boroughs.

Midlands

McLaren Building, 35 Dale End, Birmingham, B4 7NP. Tel: 0121 607 6200
The region comprises the Metropolitan Boroughs of Birmingham City, Coventry City, Dudley, Sandwell, Solihull, Walsall, Wolverhampton, and the Unitary Councils of Derby City, Leicester City, Rutland, Stoke-on-Trent City, Nottingham City, North Lincolnshire, North East Lincolnshire, and the Counties of Leicestershire, Northamptonshire, Oxfordshire, Warwickshire, Derbyshire, Lincolnshire and Nottinghamshire.

Yorkshire and North East

Woodside House, 261 Low Lane, Horsforth, Leeds LS18 5TW. Tel: 0113 2834200
The Region comprises the Metropolitan Boroughs of Barnsley, Bradford City, Calderdale, Doncaster, Gateshead, Kirklees, Leeds City, Newcastle-upon-Tyne City, North Tyneside, Rotherham, Sheffield City, South Tyneside, Sunderland, Wakefield City and the Unitary Councils of Darlington, East Riding of Yorkshire, Hartlepool, Kingston-upon-Hull City, Middlesborough, Redcar and Cleveland, Stockton-on-Tees, York and the Counties of Durham, Northumberland and North Yorkshire.

North West

Quay House, Quay Street, Manchester, M3 3JB. Tel: 0161 952 8200
The Region comprises the Metropolitan Boroughs of Bolton, Bury, Knowsley, Liverpool City, Manchester City, Oldham, Rochdale, St Helens, Salford City, Sefton, Stockport, Tameside, Trafford, Wigan, Wirral and the Unitary Councils of Blackpool, Blackburn with Darwen, Halton, Warrington and the Counties of Cheshire, Cumbria and Lancashire.

Scotland

Belford House, 59 Belford Road, Edinburgh, EH4 3UE. Tel: 0131 247 2000
The Region comprises all the Scottish Unitary authorities and island councils.

FIELD OPERATIONS DIRECTORATE:

SECTOR ORGANISATION

HSE's Field Operations Directorate (FOD) is organised on the basis of broad sector groupings, in which similar and synergistic industrial processes are brigaded together. Sectors:

- act as a focal point and help to stimulate and facilitate improvements in health, safety and welfare in the industries for which they are responsible;

- play a key role in helping FOD meet the aims and objectives of HSC/E and bring to bear the knowledge of working inspectors on sector-specific policy development and standard-setting;

- devise the best means of implementing those standards and disseminate them within HSE and the industrial sector; and

- guide the inspection activities of HSE inspectors through the sector-strategic plans which set out what should be achieved in their sector or what HSE is seeking to achieve in its interventions with sector employers.

In addition to the seven sectors, FOD has an Occupational Health and Environment (OHEU) and Safety Unit (SU) which between them deal with health and safety issues across all sectors of employment. OHEU deals with issues including: toxic substances, asbestos, biological risks, Chemical (Hazard Information and Packaging) Regulations, Notification of New Substances, respiratory protective equipment, environmental matters and all other cross-sectoral health issues. Issues dealt with by the SU include: product standards, general fire and explosion matters, carriage of dangerous, work equipment, safety signs etc.

Sector	Industries/topics covered	Region
Metals and minerals	Molten metals; ceramics and heavy clay; quarries; concrete; cement and glass	Wales and West
Services	Education; health services; Crown, fire and police; local government; docks and air transport	Home Counties
Construction	Construction	London and South East
Agriculture and wood	Agriculture; horticulture; forestry; pesticides; woodworking and sawmills	Midlands
Engineering and utilities	Engineering; shipbuilding; heavy fabrication and welding; utilities; gas safety	Midlands
Polymers and fibres	Textiles; paper and printing; rubber; plastics; leather	Yorkshire and North East
Food and entertainment	Food and drink; entertainment	Scotland

Part 2

HEALTH AND SAFETY STATISTICAL REPORT 1998/99

This part presents a summary of the latest statistics available on occupational injuries, ill health, dangerous occurrences and gas safety. Key safety statistics were published in *HSC's Safety Statistics Bulletin 1998/99* and more detailed statistics on safety and health are given in *Health and Safety Statistics 1998/99*.

INTRODUCTION

2.202   The figures presented here are principally based on RIDDOR statistics, but also draw on other sources, particularly for occupational diseases for which the RIDDOR data provide a very incomplete picture.

2.203   Information on reported fatalities is virtually complete, as a number of supplementary sources are used to complement RIDDOR reports. It is possible that a small number of fatalities, mainly to members of the public, may be missed either because of the particular circumstances of the accident or a lengthy gap between the accident and the ensuing fatality. Non-fatal injuries are significantly under-reported, although there has been an improvement in the level of reporting by employers since 1989/90.

2.204   The statistics for 1998/99 are provisional. Final figures are normally slightly higher because of late reports and because fatalities include deaths up to a year after the date of the accident. The latest information available to HSE at the time of writing has been used to provide estimated final figures for the numbers of fatalities. Estimated final figures for non-fatal injuries are based on the pattern of change over the past few years. The estimated final figures are reflected in the commentary where possible.

2.205   RIDDOR '95, which came into force on 1 April 1996, consolidated and simplified the law by applying a single set of reporting requirements to all work activities in Great Britain (including railways) and in the offshore oil and gas industry. The new Regulations also made a number of changes in the reporting requirements which has led to a lack of comparability since 1996/97 with data for earlier years.

INJURIES TO THE WORKFORCE

Overview

2.206   The number of fatal injuries to all workers (employees and self-employed combined) is expected to fall to 257 in 1998/99 compared with 274 in 1997/98. As Figure 1 shows, this number is one of the lowest in the past ten years.

2.207   The final fatal injury rate for all workers is expected to remain at 1.0 per hundred thousand workers, the lowest since the introduction of RIDDOR. Viewed over the longer term, the rate has fallen from 1.2 per hundred thousand five years ago and 1.8 in 1989/90.

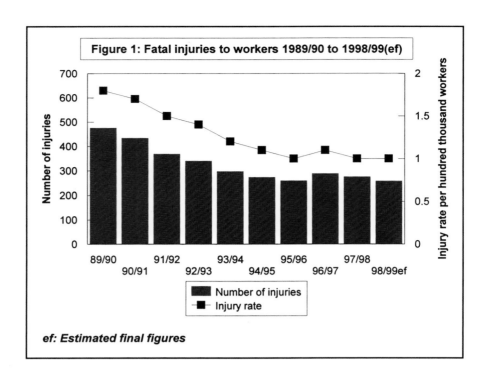

Figure 1: Fatal injuries to workers 1989/90 to 1998/99(ef)

ef: Estimated final figures

2.208 Looking at individual sectors (see Figure 2), the fatal injury rate is expected to rise in manufacturing and agriculture, but fall in the service sector and in construction. Specifically, in:

- *agriculture* the rate is likely to rise to 9.4 per hundred thousand workers;

- *manufacturing* is likely to rise to 1.7 per hundred thousand, the highest this decade;

- *construction* is likely to fall to 3.8 per hundred thousand workers, the lowest level during the 1990s;

- *services* is likely to fall to 0.3 per hundred thousand workers, again the lowest level this decade;

- *extraction and utility supply* is likely to fall from 8.0 per hundred thousand to 4.6 per hundred thousand. However, the numbers of people working in this sector are comparatively small, and this decrease represents a reduction of eight deaths in the sector.

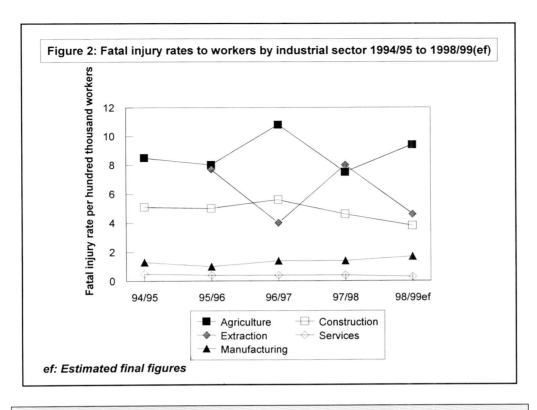

Figure 2: Fatal injury rates to workers by industrial sector 1994/95 to 1998/99(ef)

ef: Estimated final figures

Fatalities in construction

HSE has been concerned for some time that the injury rates for self-employed people in the construction industry do not necessarily give an accurate representation of the relative risk of the sector. The following statement explains the position:

> *Although only the courts can give an authoritative interpretation of law, in considering the application of these regulations and guidance to people working under another's direction, the following should be considered:*

> *If people working under the control and direction of others are treated as self-employed for tax and national insurance purposes they may nevertheless be treated as their employees for health and safety purposes. It may therefore be necessary to take appropriate action to protect them. If any doubt exists about who is responsible for the health and safety of a worker this could be clarified and included in the terms of a contract. However, remember, a legal duty under section 3 of the Health and Safety at Work Act (HSW Act) cannot be passed on by means of a contract and there will still be duties towards others under section 3 of HSW Act. If such workers are employed on the basis that they are responsible for their own health and safety, legal advice should be sought before doing so.*

Consequently, the best indication of the injury rates in the industry is obtained by looking at injuries in the combined workforce.

Employees

2.209   The fatal injury rate for employees has dropped substantially over the past 30 years. Rates in the late 1980s and early 1990s were generally less than a quarter of those at the beginning of the 1960s and less than half of those at the beginning of the 1970s. The fatal injury rate for 1997/98 is expected to fall to 0.8 per hundred thousand employees, the lowest on record.

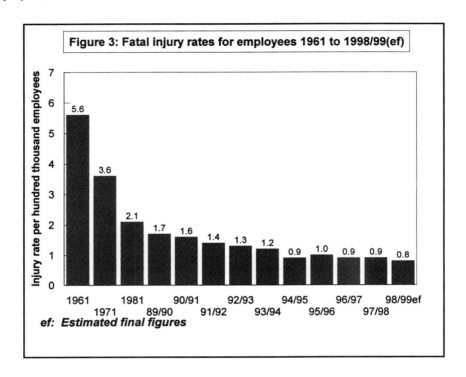

2.210   In construction, the fatal injury rate fell from 8.2 per hundred thousand to 5.7 per hundred thousand in 1997/98 and is expected to fall again in 1998/99 to 4.4 per hundred thousand. In manufacturing, the fatal injury rate has fallen from around three deaths per hundred thousand employees in the 1960s and 1970s to around two in the late 1980s and is now expected to be 1.6 per hundred thousand, although this is one of the highest levels during the 1990s. In agriculture, the fatality rate for employees is expected to fall from 6.7 per hundred thousand to 5.6 per hundred thousand. In the service sector, the fatality rate is likely to fall again from the low level of 0.4 established in 1994/95 to 0.3 per hundred thousand.

2.211   The provisional figures for 1998/99 indicate that compared with 1997/98 there were fewer deaths to employees caused by falls from a height and being struck by a moving vehicle. There was 1 fatality due to an act of violence in 1998/99, a category which only became reportable under RIDDOR '95.

2.212   Over a quarter of fatalities resulted from multiple injuries and one sixth from fractures. The number of fatalities caused by concussion and internal injuries fell from 40 in 1997/98 to 26 in 1998/99 (provisional figures).

2.213   All but 4 of the 193 fatalities reported so far were male. The number of young people (aged under 20) who died at work in 1998/99 was 6, compared with 11 in the previous year.

2.214   The numbers of fatalities in each of the constituent countries of Great Britain, England, Scotland and Wales, are expected to decrease in 1998/99. Based on provisional figures, there were 153 fatal injuries to employees in England, a decrease of 7 per cent, 27 fatalities in Scotland (one less than the previous year), and 14 fatalities in Wales, compared with 17 in 1997/98 and 22 in 1996/97.

2.215   The overall rates of fatal injury for employees from 1995/96 have been higher for Scotland and Wales than for England. With the exception of 1995/96, the overall rates of fatality for Wales were higher than those for Scotland. Trends in the number of fatal injuries and the fatal injury rates for Scotland and Wales must be treated with caution because of the relatively small number of fatalities in each country each year. Average rates of fatal injury for England, Scotland and Wales pooled over the last 4 years including provisional figures for 1998/99 were 0.8, 1.4 and 1.6 per hundred thousand respectively.

2.216   There was a reduction of five per cent in the major injury rate between 1997/98 and 1998/99.

•   The major injury rate in 1998/99 is expected to be 121.2 per hundred thousand employees.

•   The over-3-day injury rate in 1998/99 is expected to be 561.0 per hundred thousand employees, also a reduction of 5 per cent compared with the previous year.

Reporting levels of non-fatal injuries

The statistics on injuries are complemented by the information derived from the Labour Force Survey. The questions on occupational injuries in the 1990 Labour Force Survey confirmed the suspected substantial under-reporting of non-fatal injuries with around a third of reportable injuries being reported by employers. Subsequent surveys have shown that the figure has risen to about 47%, with improvements in most industries and proportionately largest changes in agriculture and the service sectors. However, the results also show that self-employed people report less than 10% of reportable injuries.

Self-employed people

2.217   The estimated final number of fatalities to the self-employed is 65, similar to the number in the previous year (62).

- The fatality rate for the self-employed is expected to be 1.9 per hundred thousand self-employed people on finalisation, compared with 1.8 in 1997/98.

- The fatality rate is expected to rise substantially in the agricultural sector from 8.7 per hundred thousand to 15.0 per hundred thousand, an increase of over 70 per cent.

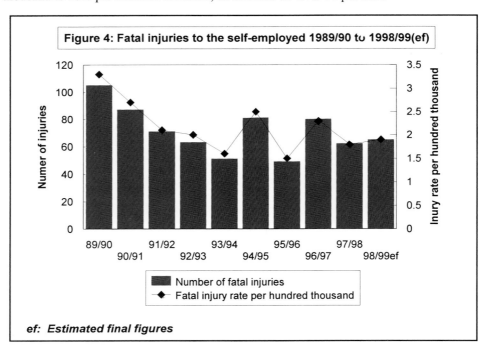

Figure 4: Fatal injuries to the self-employed 1989/90 to 1998/99(ef)

ef: Estimated final figures

INJURIES TO MEMBERS OF THE PUBLIC

2.218   The number of members of the public who suffered a fatal injury as a result of work activity is likely to be 368 in 1998/99.

2.219   Of these, 283 were fatalities on railways, including 251 suicides and trespassers. Excluding the deaths on the railways, there was little change in the number of fatalities overall compared with the previous year. The number of deaths to members of the public in agriculture is expected to be 8, three lower than in the previous year and in construction it has fallen from 6 to 4.

2.220   The number of non-fatal injuries reported to members of the public has fallen substantially, compared with last year, from 28 600 to around 23 600 in 1998/99.

ILL-HEALTH PREVALENCE AND TRENDS

The overall picture

- In 1995 an estimated 2 million individuals in Great Britain were suffering from an illness which they believed was caused by their work (current or past). 721 000 of these affected people were no longer in work. Of the remaining 1.3 million, 672 000 took no time off work, and 624 000 lost an estimated 18 million days because of work-related illness.

2.221   Our most inclusive and broadly based indications of the overall prevalence of work-related ill health are obtained from sample surveys of the national population in which people were asked whether they had any illnesses or conditions, in the twelve months prior to the survey, which had been caused or made worse by their work (current or past). HSE has carried out two such surveys in 1990 and 1995, known as SWI 90 and SWI 95 (Surveys of Self-reported Work-related Illness).

2.222   In the SWI 95 survey, respondents who reported a work-related illness were asked for permission for HSE to obtain information from the treating doctor. Such information, where obtained, usually supported the respondent's belief about work-relatedness. All individual responses were reviewed by HSE researchers and excluded from the calculated national estimates if the reported cause was implausible, taking account of the doctor's opinion when available, but not necessarily taking it as decisive.

2.223   Musculoskeletal disorders were by far the most common self-reported illness, affecting an estimated 1.2 million individuals. The second most commonly reported condition was stress, depression and anxiety, (279 000), but a further 254 000 described stress at work as causing or making their complaint worse ('stress-ascribed' condition), so that in total over 1/2 million individuals were suffering from stress or a 'stress-ascribed' condition. Over one third of the 'stress-ascribed' conditions were coded as hypertension, heart disease or stroke.

2.224   Obviously both work and non-work factors can have a role in causing illness. The frequent reporting of musculoskeletal disorders and stress may reflect increasing public awareness of the importance of these conditions and of the possibility of work factors causing them or making them worse.

2.225   Other illness categories with substantial estimated numbers affected included lower respiratory disease (202 000), deafness, tinnitus or other ear conditions (170 000), skin disease (66 000), headache or 'eyestrain' (50 000), trauma (34 000), vibration white finger (36 000), and pneumoconiosis (19 000).

2.226   Estimates of total work-related illness are available for Scotland and Wales from SWI 95, but are considerably less precise than those for Great Britain as a whole because they are derived from smaller samples. In Scotland there were an estimated 174 000 people who were suffering from a work-related illness in the twelve months prior to the survey, compared with 100 000 in Wales and 1 743 000 in England. Although the rates per head of population were slightly smaller in Scotland and Wales than in Great Britain there were no statistically significant differences between the countries.

2.227   Further information about the survey methods and more detailed results are given in the report *Self-reported work-related illness in 1995*.

2.228   Details of other sources of data, including the DSS Industrial Injuries scheme and the surveillance schemes known as SWORD, EPIDERM, MOSS, OSSA, SIDAW and OPRA, are given in the box at the end of this section. A summary of new DSS cases diagnosed in the last three years are shown in Tables 6 and 7, and figures for selected diseases from other sources which give more complete information are shown in Table 8. Numbers are much smaller than the self-reported prevalence estimates from the SWI survey, partly because they are measures of incidence (ie newly reported cases), and partly because many less serious cases are not picked up by these sources. Some of the main features and trends in recent data are summarised below; more detailed figures and commentary are given in *Health and Safety Statistics 1998/99*.

2.229   Numbers of DSS assessed cases in Scotland and Wales (Tables 6-7) reflect in some degree the different patterns of industry (current or former) in the different countries. Heavy industries which formerly employed large numbers of people in certain areas have left a legacy of industrial disease there. In 1998 60% of assessed cases in Wales were chronic bronchitis or emphysema (compared with 31% of cases in England and 24% in Scotland), obviously reflecting the former predominance of coal mining as a major industry in Wales. (The latest DSS figures for bronchitis and emphysema in Britain generally have been inflated by widening of the criteria under which former miners can claim, see the comments in the following section).   48% of assessments in Scotland were for vibration white finger (compared with 29% in England and 15% in Wales) probably reflecting the geographical distribution of the shipbuilding industry.

Diseases caused by asbestos and other mineral dusts

2.230   Deaths caused by past exposure to asbestos are mostly from cancers, either *mesothelioma* or *lung cancer*. Other diseases caused by asbestos - *asbestosis* and *non-malignant pleural disease* - can cause permanent disability but are less often fatal.

- There were 1330 deaths from mesothelioma in 1998. This was a 2% increase over the previous year's figure, but recent years are showing a smaller rate of increase than that seen earlier.   Most cases of lung cancer due to asbestos cannot be individually counted but numbers are estimated to be at least equal to mesothelioma deaths.

2.231   Because of the timing with which asbestos came into widespread use in British industry, it is the generation of men born around the Second World War and starting work in the 1950s or 1960s who will run the greatest lifetime risk of dying from mesothelioma, and numbers of such deaths in these men will increase as they age. Younger people are and will remain less at risk, benefiting from the stricter controls that were brought in by the 1969 Asbestos Regulations and the steep reduction of asbestos usage after the mid 1970s.   However the past exposures to asbestos, combined with delays of between 15 and 60 years before death, have resulted in a fairly steady increase in mesothelioma deaths from the late 1960s up to the present.

2.232   *Lung cancers* caused by asbestos are difficult to estimate accurately as most are indistinguishable from the far greater number caused by tobacco. It is believed on the basis of several studies of people exposed to asbestos that the number is probably at least equal to the number of mesotheliomas.

2.233   Coal miners are liable to lung diseases, mainly *pneumoconiosis*, which has long been compensatable under the Industrial Injuries scheme, and *chronic bronchitis or emphysema*, which was added to the list of prescribed diseases in 1993.

2.234   As with asbestosis, coalworkers' pneumoconiosis usually shows a long latent period between the start of exposure to coal dust and the diagnosis of the disease, so that present statistics reflect the industrial conditions of the past. The medical criteria prescribed by DSS for bronchitis and emphysema include a measured reduction in lung function which implies an appreciable impairment.

- There were 554 new cases of *pneumoconiosis* (excluding asbestosis) assessed under the Industrial Injuries Scheme in 1998. The increase over the previous year's figure is an artefact of the widening of the terms under which compensation is payable to coal miners for bronchitis, which resulted in many claimants for this disease being examined, and some of them being assessed as having pneumoconiosis instead. The long-term underlying trend appears to be stable or possibly falling.

- There were also 3423 assessed cases of *bronchitis or emphysema* in coal miners in 1998. The high numbers in this and the previous year compared with the figure of 269 in 1996 results from a widening of DSS medical and occupational criteria for this disease. Since compensation for bronchitis or emphysema first became available in 1993, and the numbers have been considerably affected by this widening of eligibility, there is insufficient information to assess any long-term trend.

Work-related diseases caused by other kinds of agents

- Past levels of noise in the workplace are still giving rise to claims for occupational deafness, though DSS awards have been falling for several years, with 258 new awards in 1998.

2.235   There were 3033 assessed cases of *vibration white finger* in 1997/98, caused by prolonged used of vibrating hand held tools. Numbers were similar in the two preceding years. There was a sharp increase between 1993/94 and 1995/96, but this trend is unlikely to have represented real worsening in disease incidence or working conditions, and was more likely to be due to other influences on sufferers' propensity to claim compensation.

2.236   In contrast to the mineral dust diseases mentioned above, the many substances that can cause *occupational asthma* usually do so within months of first exposure.

- SWORD returns show an estimated 869 new cases of *occupational asthma* seen by chest or occupational physicians in 1998. This is noticeably more than the numbers of DSS cases. Allowing for under-reporting in SWORD the true incidence could be at least 1500 cases a year. Trends are difficult to assess but it appears that incidence has fallen slightly since 1995-96.

101

2.237   *Occupational dermatitis* is another disease which can be caused by many chemicals in the workplace, and is probably more frequent than DSS or EPIDERM/OPRA data suggest.

- Recent reports to the EPIDERM/OPRA schemes indicate an annual average of some 3000 cases of occupational contact dermatitis seen by dermatologists or occupational physicians.   Numbers of DSS cases are much smaller (271 in 1997/98).

2.238   *Musculoskeletal disorders* affect many people, and work activities often contribute to the problem.

- An estimated 7500 new cases of work-related musculoskeletal disorders were seen by occupational physicians and rheumatologists in 1998. Both kinds of specialist reported hand, wrist or arm conditions as the most frequent sites of disorder. Occupational physicians see more disorders of the lumbar spine, while rheumatologists see more affecting the shoulder, neck, thoracic spine, ankle and foot. Numbers of cases assessed by DSS are much smaller (600 in 1997/98) and have fallen in recent years. (The kinds of disease that are compensatable by DSS are mainly restricted to upper limb disorders).

2.239   *Stress, mental health problems and infections* are also responsible for many cases of work-related illness.

- Approximately 2000 cases of work-related mental health problems are seen by occupational physicians in the OPRA reporting scheme annually. This probably significantly underestimates the true incidence of such conditions (compare the high prevalence of self-reports of work-related stress, anxiety and depression in the SWI 95 survey).

- Surveillance schemes reported approximately 1400 new cases of *occupationally acquired infections* in the year 1998, although this figure probably substantially underestimates the true incidence of occupational infections.

Data sources for work-related ill health

- There is no single comprehensive source of information for occupational and work-related disease statistics. The statistical picture must be pieced together from different sources.

- *Household surveys* yield estimates of the number of people who say that they have conditions which they believe have been caused by work. Such surveys obviously depend on lay people's perceptions of medical matters, but such perceptions are of interest in their own right, and responses can be validated in various ways. HSE has carried out two such surveys in 1990 and 1995, and the main results from the 1995 survey are presented here. This survey incorporated refinements and additions to the methods of the 1990 survey, including the seeking of confirmation and additional details from the doctors of people who report conditions. Full results have been published in the report *Self-reported work-related illness in 1995*.

- The *Industrial Injuries Scheme* administered by the Benefits Agency for the Department of Social Security (DSS) gives compensation for permanent disability from specified *'prescribed diseases'* which are conditions whose occupational cause is well established. Some kinds of occupational ill health are not covered by this scheme while others are seriously under reported. A summary of new cases diagnosed in the last three years is shown in Tables 6-7, and Table 8 shows DSS figures for selected diseases along with comparative figures from other sources where these are more complete.

- Most prescribed diseases are also reportable under RIDDOR, provided the affected employee's current job includes the work activity specifically associated with the disease, and provided the employer receives a written diagnosis from a doctor. For reportable injuries there is some under-reporting under the RIDDOR system - for reportable diseases the under-reporting is more substantial.

- *Voluntary surveillance schemes* for the reporting of work-related diseases are operated by academic medical units with HSE funding. These schemes, including those known as SWORD (Surveillance of Work-related and Occupational Respiratory Disease), EPIDERM (for work-related skin disease), MOSS (Musculoskeletal Occupational Surveillance Scheme), OSSA (Occupational Surveillance Scheme for Audiological Physicians), SIDAW (Surveillance of Infectious Disease at Work) and OPRA (Occupational Physicians Reporting Activity), count cases which are work-related in the opinion of the specialist doctor who sees them, and are co-ordinated within an Occupational Disease Intelligence Network (ODIN) based at the University of Manchester.

- *Death certificates* are useful for monitoring fatal cases of diseases caused by asbestos, and certain other occupational lung diseases.

DANGEROUS OCCURRENCES

2.240   The provisional figure for the number of dangerous occurrences reported to HSE during 1998/99 is 10 128, very similar to the number reported in 1997/98. Earlier figures cannot be compared with data for the last three years. The number of incidents reportable in respect of all workplaces fell by 100 (2 per cent), whilst the figure for specialised workplaces, ie mines, quarries, offshore and transport systems rose by 133 (2 per cent).

2.241   More than half of the dangerous occurrences reported to HSE during 1998/99 were in relation to transport systems. Of the remainder, the majority were notifiable in relation to any place of work.

- 25 per cent of these general occurrences related to failures of lifting machinery, a slightly lower proportion than last year.

GAS SAFETY

Reportable incidents

Incidents involving flammable gas supplied to premises by pipe (or refillable containers) which result in death or a specified major injury or condition, following an incident at work, are reportable under RIDDOR. These exclude injuries covered under the general provisions of RIDDOR and therefore mainly occur in domestic premises.

2.242   The number of incidents involving gas and causing injury is likely to be lower in 1998/99 than in the previous year. There have been 152 incidents reported so far.

2.243   The number of fatalities (48) is likely to be the highest since 1989/90, although there was a fall in the number of non-fatalities from 232 in 1997/98 to 222 in 1998/99.

- The number of fatalities associated with carbon monoxide poisoning is likely to be the highest since the mid 1990s. In 1998/99 there were 37 fatalities reported so far, including two suicides, compared with 28 fatalities in 1997/98, which included one suicide.

ENQUIRIES

Enquiries about statistics for injuries arising from work activity, dangerous occurrences, enforcement action and gas safety should be addressed to:

Operations Unit
Health and Safety Executive
Room 512
Daniel House
Trinity Road
Bootle
Merseyside L20 7HE

Tel: 0151 951 4842/4604

Enquiries about occupational ill health statistics should be addressed to:

Epidemiology and Medical Statistics Unit
Health and Safety Executive
Room 244
Magdalen House
Bootle
Merseyside L20 3QZ

Tel: 0151 951 4540

Table 1: Fatal injuries to all workers (employees and self-employed) as reported to all enforcing authorities by industry 1994/95 to 1998/99p

Standard Industrial Classification (1992)	1994/95	1995/96	1996/97(e)	1997/98	1998/99(p)
			Number of fatalities		
A,B Agricultural, hunting, forestry and fishing (a)	46	40	55	40	46
C,E Extractive and utility supply industries (b)	5	18	9	18	10
C Mining and quarrying (b)	4	16	7	14	6
E Electricity, gas and water supply	1	2	2	4	4
D Manufacturing	54	43	59	61	71
F Construction	83	79	90	80	66
G-Q Total service industries	84	78	74	75	65
G Wholesale and retail trade and repairs	20	23	17	17	13
H Hotels and restaurants	2	1	4	1	2
I Transport, storage and communication (c)	27	22	18	27	27
J Financial intermediation	-	-	-	-	-
K Real estate, renting and business activities	11	11	10	13	16
L Public administration and defence	9	10	8	3	2
M Education	1	2	3	-	1
N Health and social work	1	-	4	2	-
O,P,Q Other community, social and personal service activities	13	9	10	12	4
All industries	272	258	287	274	258
			Fatal injury rate (d)		
A,B Agriculture, hunting, forestry and fishing (a)	8.5	8.0	10.8	7.5	9.4
C,E Extractive and utility supply industries (b)	..	7.7	4.0	8.0	4.6
C Mining and quarrying (b)	..	22.7	9.0	17.4	7.9
E Electricity, gas and water supply	..	1.2	1.4	2.8	2.8
D Manufacturing	1.3	1.0	1.4	1.4	1.7
F Construction	5.1	5.0	5.6	4.6	3.8
G-Q Total service industries	0.5	0.4	0.4	0.4	0.3
G Wholesale and retail trade and repairs	0.5	0.6	0.4	0.4	0.3
H Hotels and restaurants	0.1	0.1	0.3	0.1	0.1
I Transport, storage and communication (c)	1.9	1.5	1.2	1.7	1.7
J Financial intermediation	-	-	-	-	-
K Real estate, renting and business activities	0.4	0.3	0.3	0.3	0.4
L Public administration and defence	0.7	0.7	0.6	0.2	0.2
M Education	0.1	0.1	0.2	-	0.1
N Health and social work	**	-	0.1	0.1	-
O,P,Q Other community, social and personal service activities	1.1	0.7	0.7	0.8	0.3
All industries	1.1	1.0	1.1	1.0	1.0

(a)   *Excludes sea fishing.*
(b)   *Includes the number of injuries in the oil and gas industry collected under offshore installations safety legislation.*
(c)   *Injuries arising from shore based services only. Excludes incidents reported under merchant shipping legislation.*
(d)   *Rate per 100 000 workers.*
(e)   *From 1996/97, injuries were reported under RIDDOR '95, prior to that they were reported under different legislation.*
..   *= Not available.*
**   *= Less than 0.05.*
p   *= provisional.*

Table 2: Fatal injuries to employees as reported to all enforcing authorities by industry 1994/95 to 1998/99p

Standard Industrial Classification (1992)	1994/95	1995/96	1996/97(e)	1997/98	1998/99(p)
			Number of fatalities		
A,B Agriculture, hunting, forestry and fishing (a)	**14**	**20**	**20**	**20**	**16**
C,E Extractive and utility supply industries (b)	**4**	**18**	**9**	**17**	**9**
C Mining and quarrying (b)	3	16	7	13	5
E Electricity, gas and water supply	1	2	2	4	4
D Manufacturing	**46**	**42**	**53**	**54**	**65**
F Construction	**58**	**62**	**66**	**58**	**48**
G-Q Total service industries	**69**	**67**	**59**	**63**	**55**
G Wholesale and retail trade and repairs	16	19	12	14	11
H Hotels and restaurants	1	1	3	-	2
I Transport, storage and communication (c)	26	21	18	26	26
J Financial intermediation	-	-	-	-	-
K Real estate, renting and business activities	6	7	3	7	11
L Public administration and defence	9	10	7	3	2
M Education	1	2	3	-	-
N Health and social work	-	-	4	1	-
O,P,Q Other community, social and personal service activities	10	7	9	12	3
All industries	**191**	**209**	**207**	**212**	**193**
			Fatal injury rate (d)		
A,B Agriculture, hunting, forestry and fishing (a)	**4.8**	**7.8**	**7.6**	**6.7**	**5.6**
C,E Extractive and utility supply industries (b)	**1.6**	**8.0**	**4.2**	**7.9**	**4.3**
C Mining and quarrying (b)	4.4	24.6	9.6	17.3	6.9
E Electricity, gas and water supply	0.6	1.3	1.4	2.9	2.9
D Manufacturing	**1.2**	**1.1**	**1.3**	**1.3**	**1.6**
F Construction	**6.9**	**7.7**	**8.2**	**5.7**	**4.4**
G-Q Total service industries	**0.4**	**0.4**	**0.4**	**0.4**	**0.3**
G Wholesale and retail trade and repairs	0.4	0.5	0.3	0.4	0.3
H Hotels and restaurants	0.1	0.1	0.2	-	0.2
I Transport, storage and communication (c)	2.0	1.7	1.4	2.0	1.9
J Financial intermediation	-	-	-	-	-
K Real estate, renting and business activities	0.2	0.3	0.1	0.2	0.3
L Public administration and defence	0.7	0.7	0.5	0.2	0.2
M Education	0.1	0.1	0.2	-	-
N Health and social work	-	-	0.2	**	-
O,P,Q Other community, social and personal service activities	1.1	0.8	0.9	1.1	0.3
All industries	**0.9**	**1.0**	**0.9**	**0.9**	**0.8**

(a)   *Excludes sea fishing.*
(b)   *Includes the number of injuries in the oil and gas industry collected under offshore installations safety legislation.*
(c)   *Injuries arising from shore based services only. Excludes incidents reported under merchant shipping legislation.*
(d)   *Rate per 100 000 employees.*
(e)   *From 1996/97, injuries were reported under RIDDOR '95, prior to that they were reported under different legislation.*
..   *= Not available.*
**   *= Less than 0.05*
p   *= provisional.*

Table 3: Fatal injuries to the self-employed as reported to all enforcing authorities by industry 1994/95 to 1998/99p

Standard Industrial Classification (1992)	1994/95	1995/96	1996/97(e)	1997/98	1998/99(p)
			Number of fatalities		
A,B Agriculture, hunting, forestry and fishing (a)	32	20	35	20	30
C,E Extractive and utility supply industries (b)	1	-	-	1	1
C Mining and quarrying (b)	1	-	-	1	1
E Electricity, gas and water supply	-	-	-	-	-
D Manufacturing	8	1	6	7	6
F Construction	25	17	24	22	18
G-Q Total service industries	15	11	15	12	10
G Wholesale and retail trade and repairs	4	4	5	3	2
H Hotels and restaurants	1	-	1	1	-
I Transport, storage and communication (c)	1	1	-	1	1
J Financial intermediation	-	-	-	-	-
K Real estate, renting and business activities	5	4	7	6	5
L Public administration and defence	-	-	1	-	-
M Education	-	-	-	-	1
N Health and social work	1	-	-	1	-
O,P,Q Other community, social and personal service activities	3	2	1	-	1
All industries	81	49	80	62	65
			Fatal injury rate (d)		
A,B Agriculture, hunting, forestry and fishing (a)	12.9	8.3	14.3	8.7	15.0
C,E Extractive and utility supply industries (b)	..	-	-	10.3	13.0
C Mining and quarrying (b)	..	-	-	19.3	34.6
E Electricity, gas and water supply	..	-	-	-	-
D Manufacturing	3.2	0.4	2.3	2.7	2.2
F Construction	3.2	2.2	3.0	3.1	2.8
G-Q Total service industries	0.8	0.6	0.7	0.5	0.4
G Wholesale and retail trade and repairs	0.7	0.8	1.0	0.6	0.4
H Hotels and restaurants	0.6	-	-	0.6	-
I Transport, storage and communication (c)	0.6	0.5	-	0.5	0.5
J Financial intermediation	-	-	-	-	-
K Real estate, renting and business activities	1.1	0.8	1.3	1.1	0.9
L Public administration and defence	-	-	9.6	-	-
M Education	-	-	-	-	0.9
N Health and social work	0.5	-	-	0.4	-
O,P,Q Other community, social and personal service activities	1.1	0.7	0.3	-	0.2
All industries	2.5	1.5	2.3	1.8	1.9

(a) *Excludes sea fishing.*
(b) *Includes the number of injuries in the oil and gas industry collected under offshore installations safety legislation.*
(c) *Injuries arising from shore based services only. Excludes incidents reported under merchant shipping legislation.*
(d) *Rate per 100 000 self-employed.*
(e) *From 1996/97, injuries were reported under RIDDOR '95, prior to that they were reported under different legislation.*
.. *= Not available.*
** *= Less than 0.05.*
p *= provisional.*

Table 4: Fatal injuries to members of the public as reported to all enforcing authorities by industry 1994/95 to 1998/99p

Standard Industrial Classification (1992)	1994/95	1995/96	1996/97(d)	1997/98	1998/99(p)
			Number of fatalities		
A,B Agriculture, hunting, forestry and fishing (a)	5	5	9	11	8
C,E Extractive and utility supply industries (b)	4	3	3	1	2
C Mining and quarrying (b)	2	-	3	-	1
E Electricity, gas and water supply	2	3	-	1	1
D Manufacturing	2	-	1	1	-
F Construction	5	3	3	6	4
G-Q Total service industries	88	75	351	374	352
G Wholesale and retail trade and repairs	1	2	3	2	2
H Hotels and restaurants	6	-	-	1	3
I Transport, storage and communication (c)	9	3	277	312	288
J Financial intermediation	-	-	-	-	-
K Real estate, renting and business activities	3	2	1	1	2
L Public administration and defence	1	3	5	9	6
M Education	9	2	7	3	5
N Health and social work	49	48	45	35	37
O,P,Q Other community, social and personal service activities	10	15	13	11	9
All industries	104	86	367	393	366

(a)   Excludes sea fishing.
(b)   Includes the number of injuries in the oil and gas industry collected under offshore installations safety legislation.
(c)   Injuries arising from shore based services only. Excludes incidents reported under merchant shipping legislation.
(d)   From 1996/97, includes fatalities to members of the public on railways (including suicides and trespassers) which were previously reported under separate railway legislation and are now reportable under RIDDOR '95.

p   =   provisional.

Table 5: Total numbers of fatal injuries as reported to all enforcing authorities by industry 1994/95 to 1998/99p

Standard Industrial Classification (1992)	1994/95	1995/96	1996/97(d)	1997/98	1998/99(p)
			Number of fatalities		
A,B Agriculture, hunting, forestry and fishing (a)	51	45	64	51	54
C,E Extractive and utility supply industries (b)	9	21	12	19	12
C Mining and quarrying (b)	6	16	10	14	7
E Electricity, gas and water supply	3	5	2	5	5
D Manufacturing	56	43	60	62	71
F Construction	88	82	93	86	70
G-Q Total service industries	172	153	425	449	417
G Wholesale and retail trade and repairs	21	25	20	19	15
H Hotels and restaurants	8	1	4	2	5
I Transport, storage and communication (c)	36	25	295	339	315
J Financial intermediation	-	-	-	-	-
K Real estate, renting and business activities	14	13	11	14	18
L Public administration and defence	10	13	13	12	8
M Education	10	4	10	3	6
N Health and social work	50	48	49	37	37
O,P,Q Other community, social and personal service activities	23	24	23	23	13
All industries	376	344	654	667	624

(a)   Excludes sea fishing.
(b)   Includes the number of injuries in the oil and gas industry collected under offshore installations safety legislation.
(c)   Injuries arising from shore based services only. Excludes incidents reported under merchant shipping legislation.
(d)   From 1996/97, injuries were reported under RIDDOR '95 which replaced previous legislation. From 1996/97, includes fatalities to members of the public on railways (including suicides and trespassers) which were previously reported under railway legislation.
p =   provisional

Table 6: Prescribed industrial diseases; cases of occupational lung disease assessed for Disablement Benefit in England, Wales and Scotland, 1996-1998

	Disease	Disease No	1996	1997	1998
England	Pneumoconiosis	D1			
	coal		242	145	441
	asbestos		337	269	225
	other		26	30	47
	Diffuse Mesothelioma	D3	539	475	500
	Occupational Asthma	D7	318	223	175
	Lung cancer with asbestosis/pleural thickening	D8	38	21	36
	Pleural thickening	D9	134	130	187
	Chronic Bronchitis or emphysema [1]	D12	118	1 938	2 312
	Others		12	5	7
	Total		1 764	3 236	3 930

Table 6 continues on p 111.

	Disease	Disease No	1996	1997	1998
Wales	Pneumoconiosis	D1			
	coal		72	52	35
	asbestos		32	16	34
	other		8	7	15
	Diffuse Mesothelioma	D3	17	17	19
	Occupational Asthma	D7	44	31	23
	Lung cancer with asbestosis/pleural	D8	3	1	4
	Pleural thickening	D9	15	12	19
	Chronic Bronchitis or emphysema [1]	D12	147	765	743
	Others		1	1	2
	Total		339	902	894
Scotland	Pneumoconiosis	D1			
	coal		7	6	9
	asbestos		105	54	56
	other		5	8	7
	Diffuse Mesothelioma	D3	76	53	64
	Occupational Asthma	D7	48	43	24
	Lung cancer with asbestosis/pleural	D8	6	3	1
	Pleural thickening	D9	18	13	20
	Chronic Bronchitis or emphysema [1]	D12	4	324	356
	Others		-	-	-
	Total		269	504	537
Great Britain	Pneumoconiosis	D1			
	coal		323	204	485
	asbestos		479	344	316
	other		39	45	69
	Diffuse Mesothelioma	D3	642	553	590
	Occupational Asthma	D7	410	298	222
	Lung cancer with asbestosis/pleural	D8	51	26	42
	Pleural thickening	D9	168	156	227
	Chronic Bronchitis or emphysema [1]	D12	269	3 030	3 423
	Others		13	6	9
	Total		2 394	4 662	5 383

Source: DSS

Notes:

Figures for Great Britain include a small number of cases not included in England, Wales and Scotland breakdowns. These individuals developed industrial diseases from employment in Great Britain, but are currently residing overseas.

Figures are for calendar years.

*(1)	The high number of bronchitis and emphysema cases in 1997-98 are the result of widening of the DSS eligibility criteria - see paragraph 2.234 of the text.*

Table 7: Prescribed industrial diseases; cases of occupational non-lung diseases assessed for Disablement Benefit in England, Wales and Scotland, October 1995 to September 1998

	Disease	Disease No	1995/6	1996/7	1997/8
England	Musculoskeletal [1]	A4 - A8	762	648	509
	Occupational deafness	A10	421	297	176
	Vibration white finger	A11	2 353	2 309	2 135
	Carpal tunnel syndrome	A12	236	244	312
	Allergic Rhinitis	D4	693	309	163
	Dermatitis	D5	267	276	199
	Others		63	71	65
	Total		4 795	4 154	3 559
Wales	Musculoskeletal [1]	A4 - A8	39	37	27
	Occupational deafness	A10	50	23	26
	Vibration white finger	A11	88	194	190
	Carpal tunnel syndrome	A12	10	20	25
	Allergic Rhinitis	D4	25	41	30
	Dermatitis	D5	19	21	34
	Others		1	5	7
	Total		232	341	339
Scotland	Musculoskeletal [1]	A4 - A8	70	79	64
	Occupational deafness	A10	60	93	55
	Vibration white finger	A11	574	785	707
	Carpal tunnel syndrome	A12	17	33	63
	Allergic Rhinitis	D4	2	2	5
	Dermatitis	D5	42	39	37
	Others		15	9	11
	Total		780	1 040	942
Great Britain	Musculoskeletal [1]	A4 - A8	871	764	600
	Occupational deafness	A10	531	413	258
	Vibration white finger	A11	3 016	3 288	3 033
	Carpal tunnel syndrome	A12	265	297	400
	Allergic Rhinitis	D4	720	352	199
	Dermatitis	D5	328	336	271
	Others		79	85	83
	Total		5 810	5 535	4 844

Source: DSS

Notes:

(1)   Mainly upper-limb disorders

Figures are for years ending 30 September, except for occupational deafness where calendar years 1996 to 1998 are shown.

Figures for Great Britain include a small number of cases not included in England, Wales and Scotland breakdowns. These individuals developed industrial diseases from employment in Great Britain, but are currently residing overseas.

Table 8: Comparison of cases assessed for Disablement Benefit with figures from other surveillance schemes: Selected diseases, Great Britain 1997-1998.

	Industrial Injuries Scheme			Other Surveillance Schemes	
	1997	**1998**		**1997**	**1998**
Mesothelioma	553	590	DCs [4]	1 330p	..
Asthma	298	222	SWORD/OPRA	1 031	869
Farmer's lung, allergic alveolitis	4	4	SWORD/OPRA	59	29
Hearing loss	413	258	OSSA/OPRA [1]	1 016	929
	1996/97[3]	**1997/98**[3]			
Vibration white finger and carpal tunnel syndrome	3 585	3 433	MOSS/OPRA [1,2]	203	689
Other upper limb disorders	635	514	MOSS/OPRA [1,2]	3 640	4 305
Dermatitis	336	271	EPIDERM/OPRA	3 124	3 571
Infections	13	17	SIDAW	1 261	1 398

Sources: DSS, ONS, GRO(S), ODIN

p   *Provisional*

..   *Not yet available*

(1)   The OSSA and MOSS schemes began to collect reports in the last quarter of 1997; the MOSS/OSSA cases have therefore been multiplied by four and added to the OPRA cases to produce an annual estimate for this year.

(2)   Some cases reported in MOSS/OPRA suffered from VWF/CTS and other upper limb disorders also, and were counted in both categories.

(3)   Year ending 30 September.

(4)   Death certificates mentioning mesothelioma.

Part 3

HEALTH AND SAFETY COMMISSION,

HEALTH AND SAFETY EXECUTIVE

ACCOUNTS 1998/99

FOREWORD

1   Background information

The Health and Safety at Work etc Act 1974 provided for the creation of a Health and Safety Commission (HSC) and Health and Safety Executive (HSE) and the continuation of the Employment Medical Advisory Service. The Commission came into being on 1 October 1974 and appointed the Health and Safety Executive on 1 January 1975. The aims of the Commission and the Executive, whose existence and functions derive from the 1974 Act, are to protect the health, safety and welfare of employees and to safeguard others, principally the public, who may be exposed to risks from work activities. For further information refer to paragraphs 1.70 to 1.158 of the Annual Report.

The financial statements of the Commission and Executive have been prepared pursuant to paragraphs 14(1) and 20 of Schedule 2 of the Health and Safety at Work etc Act 1974 in a form determined by the Secretary of State with the approval of the Treasury. They are commercial style accrual financial statements which show the full in year resource costs of the Commission and Executive. They are not control accounts: the Commission is controlled on cash spend against Voted provision; details of which are contained in Note 19 and paragraph 1.165 of the Annual Report.

2   Results and appropriations

The total grant in aid received by the Commission was £177 500 000 and after operating costs of £547 512 the balance of £176 952 488 was passed to the Executive. The operating deficit was £1 673 664 and after loss on disposal of fixed assets of £182 856 and the notional interest adjustment of £2 327 775, the result was a deficit for the year of £1 856 520 which was transferred to the Income and Expenditure Account.

An operating result does not represent a cash underspend/overspend as income is recognised when earned and expenditure when incurred and includes some non-cash costs, rather than being purely on a cash received or cash paid basis.

Surrenders to the Consolidated Fund are shown in Note 3 and a statement on working balances is shown in Note 18.

3   Review of activities

The continuing aims and key priorities for 1998/99 of the HSC and HSE are reviewed in Sections 1 and 2 of the Annual Report.

4   Market value of land and buildings

The leasehold property at Rose Court, Southwark, London was independently valued in 1997/98 by Thompson Yates, Chartered Surveyors as having a value of £2 125 000, the balance sheet carrying value being nil, in accordance with accounting policy note 1(f).

The leasehold properties, St Hugh's House, Bootle and the site at the National Agricultural Centre, Stoneleigh were independently valued in 1996/97 by Derrick, Wade and Waters, Chartered Surveyors and ET Parker, Chartered Surveyors, respectively.

The freehold and leasehold properties at Sheffield and Buxton were last independently valued in 1995/96 by Grimley, Chartered Surveyors. The property at Carlisle was transferred to HSE on 1 April 1996 from Property Holdings, Department of the Environment and independently valued in 1995/96 by Property Holdings. In each case the basis of valuation was open market value with existing use with the exception of Buxton, which was on the basis of depreciated replacement cost. In all cases the valuations were in accordance with the Appraisal and Valuation Manual of the Royal Institute of Chartered Surveyors. In the periods between formal valuations properties have been revalued in accordance with appropriate indices, as described in accounting policy note 1(c).

There is no significant difference between the book values and the market values of land and buildings included in these Accounts with the exception of Rose Court, Southwark Bridge, London.

Details of Fixed Assets are disclosed in Note 7 of the HSE Notes to the Accounts.

5   Research and development

HSE's research and development and technical support is detailed in paragraphs 1.147 to 1.150 of the Annual Report.

6   Future development

The Commission's and Executive's continuing aims and key priorities for 1998/99 were set out in the Health and Safety Commission's Plan of Work published in May 1998.

7   Health and Safety Commission members

Chairman : Sir Frank Davies CBE, OStJ

Other members: George Brumwell, Margaret Burns, David Coulston, Joyce Edmond-Smith, Anne Gibson, Michael McKiernan, Rex Symons CBE, Owen Tudor and Robin Turney.

Alan Grant resigned on 16 November 1998. Owen Tudor was appointed from 17 November 1998. David Coulston's and Robin Turney's appointments ended on 31 March 1999. Abdul Chowdry and Sonny Hamid were appointed from 1 April 1999.

8   Health and Safety Executive members

Director General: Jenny Bacon CB.

Other members: David Eves CB and Richard Hillier.

9   Corporate Governance

The Health and Safety Commission and the Health and Safety Executive are committed to supporting the recommendations of the Cadbury Committee on the Financial Aspects of Corporate Governance to the extent that the Code can be applied to the Public Sector.

HSC comprises a Chairman and nine members who are all the equivalent of independent non executive directors (for full details refer pages (v) and (vi) in the Annual Report). They are appointed on a fixed term basis (refer note 3 and note 5 in the respective Notes to the Accounts) with no automatic right of reappointment. The appointments are made by the Secretary of State and as regards the members after consultation with organisations representing employers, employees, local authorities and other relevant bodies.

HSE comprises a Director (Director General) and two other members who are all the equivalent of executive directors (see page vii of the Annual Report). They are all appointed by the Commission with approval of the Secretary of State and the two other members after consultation with the Director General.

The general functions of the Commission and the Executive are specified in the Health and Safety at Work etc Act 1974 the latter being primarily responsible for operational matters. Each of the Boards meet regularly to discuss strategic direction and plans, formulate policy on key issues etc in order to maintain full and effective control over all significant policy, regulation and guidance, compliance, organisational and financial issues (refer also to the Foreword in the Annual Report).

Throughout the year and in all material respects, the Executive complied with the terms of the financial memorandum issued by the Secretary of State for the Environment, Transport and the Regions.

A separate statement is made on the system of internal financial control.

10   Equal opportunities

The Executive is an Equal Opportunities Employer with a determination to treat all people fairly, irrespective of gender, ethnic origin, marital status, religious belief, age, sexual orientation or disability. Details of the Executive's Equal Opportunities Programme are shown in paragraph 1.173 of the Annual Report.

11   Employee involvement

There are well established consultation arrangements in HSE for recognised trade unions to contribute to all matters affecting the staff. Staff involvement is actively encouraged as part of day to day line management and continuous efforts are being made to improve methods and channels of communication.

Staff development and training continued to have high priority with the emphasis on meeting HSE's business needs and ultimately the goal of achieving the Investors in People (IiP) standard. Further details are shown in paragraphs 1.172 to 1.173 of the Annual Report.

12   Prompt payments

The Health and Safety Executive is committed to the prompt payment of bills for goods and services received and conforms to the principles of the CBI Code on prompt payments. Payments are normally made as specified in the contract. If there is no contractual provision, or other understanding, payment is due to be made within 30 days of the receipt of the goods or services or presentation of a valid invoice or similar demand, whichever is later. HSE's overall performance during 1998/99 was 94% (1997/98 89%) of invoices paid within the agreed credit period.

13   Health and safety within HSE

The Executive aims to set and maintain exemplary standards of performance so as to ensure the health and safety of its staff, as well as others who may work on or visit its premises. Further details are shown in paragraphs 1.174 to 1.180 of the Annual Report.

14   Environment

HSE has continued to pursue and promote best environmental practice and to implement initiatives set out in the Government's White Paper. Further details are shown in paragraphs 1.76 and 1.181 of the Annual Report.

15   Year 2000 issues

Comments on year 2000 issues are made in paragraph 1.199 to 1.201 of the Annual Report.

16   Introduction of the Euro

The third stage of European Economic and Monetary Union (EMU) was reached on 1 January 1999 with the introduction of a single currency, the euro. A euro working party has been established to review our procedures and systems in order to facilitate trading in the euro in line with the National Change Over Plan.

We have a small number and value of transactions both with countries that entered the common currency system and other countries. Its introduction is not expected to have a significant effect.

All related costs will be written off through the Income & Expenditure account as they are incurred.

17   Post balance sheet events

The Health and Safety Laboratory is actively considering a co-location of its Sheffield and Buxton premises. As part of the procurement process the Private Finance Initiative option is being pursued. Consortia bids have been received and evaluated. A preferred bidder (Investors in the Community (Buxton) Ltd) has been selected. Contractual and financial terms are being negotiated. The bid proposal is being compared with the Public Sector comparator to achieve an affordable value for money solution.

18   Auditors

The financial statements of the Commission and Executive are audited under Schedule 2 paragraph 14(2) and 20 of the Health and Safety at Work etc Act 1974 by the Comptroller and Auditor General.

Jenny Bacon CB
Director General, Health and Safety Executive
Accounting Officer   29 September 1999

Sir Frank Davies CBE, OStJ
Chairman, Health and Safety Commission
Accounting Officer   29 September 1999

STATEMENT OF THE COMMISSION'S, THE EXECUTIVE'S, THE CHAIRMAN'S AND DIRECTOR GENERAL'S RESPONSIBILITIES

Under paragraphs 14(1) and 20(1) of Schedule 2 of the Health and Safety at Work etc Act 1974 the Health and Safety Commission and the Health and Safety Executive are required to prepare a statement of accounts for each financial year in the form and on the basis determined by the Secretary of State, with the consent of the Treasury as set out in the accounts directions at Appendix A and B to these financial statements. The accounts are prepared on an accruals basis and must give a true and fair view of the Commission's and Executive's state of affairs at the year end and of their income and expenditure and cash flows for the financial year.

In preparing their accounts the Commission and Executive are required to:

- observe the accounts directions issued by the Secretary of State, including the relevant accounting and disclosure requirements, and apply suitable accounting policies on a consistent basis;

- make judgements and estimates on a reasonable basis;

- state whether applicable accounting standards have been followed, and disclose and explain any material departures in the financial statements;

- prepare the financial statements on the going concern basis, unless it is inappropriate to presume that the Commission and the Executive will continue in operation.

The Accounting Officer for the Department of the Environment, Transport and the Regions has designated the Chairman of the Health and Safety Commission and the Director General of the Health and Safety Executive as Accounting Officers for the Commission and Executive respectively. Their relevant responsibilities as Accounting Officers, including their responsibilities for the propriety and regularity of the public finances for which they are answerable and for the keeping of proper records are set out in the Non-Departmental Public Bodies' Accounting Officer Memorandum, issued by the Treasury and published in Government Accounting.

Jenny Bacon CB
Director General, Health and Safety Executive
Accounting Officer   29 September 1999

Sir Frank Davies CBE, OStJ
Chairman, Health and Safety Commission
Accounting Officer   29 September 1999

STATEMENT ON THE SYSTEM OF INTERNAL FINANCIAL CONTROL

As Accounting Officers (in the case of HSC, the Chairman and for the HSE, the Director General) we acknowledge our respective responsibilities for ensuring that an effective system of internal financial control is maintained and operated for HSC and HSE. The system can provide only reasonable and not absolute assurance that assets are safeguarded, that transactions are authorised and properly recorded, and that material errors or irregularities are either prevented or would be detected within a timely period.

The system of internal financial control is based on a framework of regular management information, financial regulations, administrative procedures including the segregation of duties, and various levels of delegation specified by HM Treasury, Department of the Environment, Transport and the Regions and the Executive Board.

In particular, it includes:

- comprehensive budgeting systems with an annual budget which is approved by the Executive Board;

- regular reviews by the Executive Board of monthly and annual financial reports which indicate financial performance against the forecast;

- setting and monitoring targets to measure financial and a range of other business performance objectives;

- procedures for the Executive Board to review and agree the budgets;

- clearly defined capital investment control guidelines;

- as appropriate, formal project management disciplines;

HSE has an internal audit unit, which operates to standards defined in the Government Internal Audit Manual, with the right of direct access to the Accounting Officer of both the Commission and Executive. The work of the internal audit unit is informed by an analysis of the risk to which the organisations are exposed, and annual internal audit plans are based on this analysis. The analysis of risk and the internal audit plans are endorsed by the HSE Audit Committee which meets regularly and comprises all members of the Executive and the Head of Planning, Efficiency and Finance Division. These plans are approved by us. The Head of Internal Audit provides the Committee annually with a report on internal audit activity in the organisations, including an independent opinion on the adequacy and effectiveness of the organisations' systems of internal financial control.

The review of the effectiveness of the system of internal financial control is thus conducted through mechanisms noted above via the Executive and the Audit Committee, together with the work of the internal auditors and the executive managers within the organisations who have responsibility for the development and maintenance of the financial control framework and comment made by the external auditors in their management letter and other reports.

Jenny Bacon CB
Director General, Health and Safety Executive
Accounting Officer   29 September 1999

Sir Frank Davies CBE, OStJ
Chairman, Health and Safety Commission
Accounting Officer   29 September 1999

HEALTH AND SAFETY COMMISSION
THE CERTIFICATE AND REPORT OF THE COMPTROLLER AND AUDITOR GENERAL TO THE HOUSES OF PARLIAMENT

I certify that I have audited the financial statements on pages 127 to 132 under the Health and Safety at Work etc Act 1974. These financial statements have been prepared under the historical cost convention and the accounting policies set out on page 128.

Respective responsibilities of the Commission, Chairman, and Auditor

As described on page 122 the Chairman of the Health and Safety Commission is responsible for the preparation of the financial statements and for ensuring the regularity of financial transactions. The Chairman and the Director General of the Health and Safety Executive are jointly responsible for the preparation of the other contents of the Annual Report. My responsibilities, as independent auditor, are guided by the Auditing Practices Board and the auditing profession's ethical guidance.

I report my opinion as to whether the financial statements give a true and fair view and are properly prepared in accordance with the Health and Safety at Work etc Act 1974 and directions made thereunder by the Secretary of State, and whether in all material respects the expenditure and income have been applied to the purposes intended by Parliament and the financial transactions conform to the authorities which govern them. I also report if, in my opinion, the Foreword is not consistent with the financial statements, if the Commission has not kept proper accounting records, or if I have not received all the information and explanations I require for my audit.

I read the other information contained in the Annual Report and consider whether it is consistent with the audited financial statements. I consider the implications for my certificate if I become aware of any apparent misstatements or material inconsistencies with the financial statements.

I review whether the joint statement on pages 123 and 124 reflects the Commission's compliance with Treasury's guidance 'Corporate governance: statement on the system of internal financial control'. I report if it does not meet the requirements specified by Treasury, or if the statement is misleading or inconsistent with other information I am aware of from my audit of the financial statements.

Basis of opinion

I conducted my audit in accordance with Auditing Standards issued by the Auditing Practices Board. An audit includes examination, on a test basis, of evidence relevant to the amounts, disclosures and regularity of financial transactions included in the financial statements. It also includes an assessment of the significant estimates and judgements made by the Chairman in the preparation of the financial statements, and of whether the accounting policies are appropriate to the Commission's circumstances, consistently applied and adequately disclosed.

I planned and performed my audit so as to obtain all the information and explanations which I considered necessary in order to provide me with sufficient evidence to give reasonable assurance that the financial statements are free from material misstatement, whether caused by error, or by fraud or other irregularity and that, in all material respects, the expenditure and income have been applied to the purposes intended by Parliament and the financial transactions conform to the authorities which govern them. In forming my opinion I also evaluated the overall adequacy of the presentation of information in the financial statements.

Opinion

In my opinion:

- the financial statements give a true and fair view of the state of affairs of the Health and Safety Commission at 31 March 1999 and of the amount transferred to the Health and Safety Executive and have been properly prepared in accordance with the Health and Safety at Work etc Act 1974 and with the directions made thereunder by the Secretary of State; and

- in all material respects the expenditure and income have been applied to the purposes intended by Parliament and the financial transactions conform to the authorities which govern them.

I have no observations to make on these financial statements.

John Bourn
Comptroller and Auditor General
National Audit Office
157-197 Buckingham Palace Road
London
SW1W 9SP

15 October 1999

HEALTH AND SAFETY COMMISSION: INCOME AND EXPENDITURE ACCOUNT FOR THE YEAR ENDED 31 MARCH 1999

	Notes	£'000	£'000	1997/98 £'000
Income				
Grant in aid:				
Received from Department of the Environment, Transport and the Regions	2		177 500	178 600
Expenditure				
Staff costs	3a	288		279
Other operating charges	3g	260		231
Allocation of grant in aid to Health and Safety Executive	2	176 952		178 090
			177 500	178 600
			-	-

All operations were continuing operations throughout 1998/99 and there were no material acquisitions or disposals in the year.

There are no material balances as at 31 March 1999 and a Balance Sheet has therefore not been prepared.

The notes on pages 128 to 132 form part of this account

Sir Frank Davies CBE, OStJ

Chairman, Health and Safety Commission
Accounting Officer

29 September 1999

HEALTH AND SAFETY COMMISSION: NOTES TO THE ACCOUNTS

1   Accounting policies

(a)   Accounts Directions

In accordance with Accounts Directions issued by the Secretary of State with the approval of the Treasury, the Health and Safety Commission and Health and Safety Executive have prepared a joint Foreword and separate Income and Expenditure Accounts. Any assets and liabilities relevant to HSC, are included in the HSE Balance Sheet (Schedule 2). These are not material in value.

(b)   Accounting Convention

The accounts meet the accounting and disclosure requirements of the Companies Acts and accounting standards issued or adopted by the Accounting Standards Board and accounting disclosure requirements issued by HM Treasury from time to time, in so far as these requirements are appropriate. Consolidated accounts have not been prepared, with the agreement of HM Treasury and National Audit Office, on the basis that there is a statutory requirement to produce separate accounts for HSC and HSE and it would be administratively burdensome and provide no additional information for the reader of the accounts.

(c)   Pension Costs

The current Chairman is not a member of the Principal Civil Service Pension Scheme (PCSPS) but arrangements exist whereby the Health and Safety Executive make pension payments analogous to those that would have been made if he had been a member of the PCSPS.

The appointment of Commission members is non-pensionable.

The employees of the Health and Safety Commission, other than the Chairman and Commission members, are Civil Servants to whom the conditions of the Superannuation Acts 1965 and 1972 and subsequent amendments apply. The staff are covered by the PCSPS which is a non-contributory scheme. The rate of the employers contribution is determined by the Government Actuary and advised by the Treasury and is charged to the Income and Expenditure Account.

For 1998/99 the rates of superannuation for non-industrial staff apply according to grade at 12%, 13.5%, 16.5% and 18.5%.

In addition, the Health and Safety Commission operates an Early Retirement Scheme which gives retirement benefits to certain qualifying employees. These benefits conform to the rules of the PCSPS. The Health and Safety Commission and Executive bear the costs of these benefits until the normal retiring age of the employees who have retired under the Early Retirement Scheme.

The total pensions liability up to retiring age of each employee is charged to the Income and Expenditure Account in the year in which the employees takes early retirement.

2   Grant in aid

Pursuant to Section 43 of the Health and Safety at Work etc Act 1974, the Commission is financed by a grant in aid borne on a Vote of the Department of the Environment, Transport and the Regions (Class VI Vote 5).

The total grant in aid received by the Health and Safety Commission from the Department of the Environment, Transport and the Regions for the financial year 1998/99 was £177 500 000 and after deducting £287 546 for staff costs and £259 966 for other operating charges the sum of £176 952 488 was allocated to the Health and Safety Executive.

3   Expenditure of the Health and Safety Commission

This is stated after charging:

			1997/98
		£'000	£'000
(a) Staff costs of the Health and Safety Commission:			
Wages and salaries		232	227
Social Security costs		18	16
Superannuation costs		17	16
Pension costs		21	20
		288	279

(b) Emoluments of the Chairman:					1997/98
	Salary	Pension contributions	Other taxable benefits	Total	Total
	£	£	£	£	£
Frank Davies CBE, OStJ	63 412	-	23 774	87 186	74 844

Notes.

Other taxable benefits for the Chairman include mileage, a contribution to chauffeur's costs and an accommodation allowance as appropriate. Any ensuing tax liability is met by HSC.

(c)   Emoluments of the Commission members:

	Notes	Salary	Fees	Other taxable benefits	Total	1997/98 Total
		£	£	£	£	£
Cynthia Atwell	1	-	-	-	-	7 037
George Brumwell		1 279	2 695	16	3 990	-
Margaret Burns		1 279	5 197	2 708	9 184	-
David Coulston	2	1 279	4 065	2 547	7 891	4 576
Joyce Edmond-Smith		1 279	7 042	426	8 747	6 578
Anne Gibson		1 279	2 500	-	3 779	3 982
Alan Grant	3	849	2 216	-	3 065	4 694
Michael McKiernan		1 279	4 786	1 863	7 928	8 237
Ann Scully OBE	4	-	-	-	-	3 356
Rex Symons CBE		1 279	5 405	1 556	8 240	9 111
Owen Tudor	5	537	1 781	-	2 318	-
Robin Turney	6	1 279	5 591	1 928	8 798	6 960
		11 618	41 278	11 044	63 940	54 531

Notes:

1.   Appointment ended 31 March 1998

2.   Appointment ended 31 March 1999

3.   Resigned 16 November 1998

4.   Died November 1997

5.   Appointed 17 November 1998

6.   Appointment ended 31 March 1999

Other taxable benefits for Commission members include mileage and an accommodation allowance, as appropriate. Any ensuing tax liability is met by HSC.

The Chairman and Commission members are appointed for a fixed term for up to three years. The Chairman is part-time working three days a week. If they cease to be a member or Chairman, other than on the expiry of the term of office, and it appears to the Secretary of State that there are special circumstances which justify the payment of compensation, a payment can be made as determined by the Secretary of State with Treasury approval.

(d) Pensions to previous Chairmen:		1997/98
	£	£
Sir John Cullen	12 591	12 154
Sir William Simpson	8 151	7 867
	20 742	20 021

		1997/98
	No.	No.
(e) Emoluments of staff, other than the Chairman and Commission members falling within the following range:		
£40 000 - £49 999	-	-

The average number of employees during the year of the account, other than the Chairman and Commission members was made up as follows:

	No.	No.
Non-specialist staff	5	5

(f)   Related Party Transactions

The Health and Safety Commission is an Executive Non-Departmental Public Body with Crown status and is sponsored by the Department of the Environment, Transport and the Regions (DETR).

DETR is regarded as a related party. During the year, HSC did not have any material transactions with DETR or other entities for which the DETR is regarded as the parent Department.

None of the Commission members or any persons connected with them have any interest in any material transactions with HSC/HSE during the year.

			1997/98
(g)	Other operating costs of the Health and Safety Commission:	**£'000**	£'000
	General administrative expenses	**66**	76
	Travel, subsistence and hospitality for:		
	Chairman, Commission members and support staff (see note below)	**124**	82
	Rent, rates, maintenance and other premises costs	**70**	73
		260	231

Note: Travel, subsistence and hospitality expenses for the Chairman and Commission members was £90 341 (1997/98 £54 020), whilst the total for the support staff was £33 664 (1997/98 £27 857).

HEALTH AND SAFETY EXECUTIVE
THE CERTIFICATE AND REPORT OF THE COMPTROLLER AND
AUDITOR GENERAL TO THE HOUSES OF PARLIAMENT

I certify that I have audited the financial statements on pages 135 to 158 under the Health and Safety at Work etc Act 1974. These financial statements have been prepared under the historical cost convention as modified by the revaluation of certain fixed assets and the accounting policies set out on pages 140 to 144.

Respective responsibilities of the Executive, Director General and Auditor

As described on page 122 the Director General of the Health and Safety Executive is responsible for the preparation of the financial statements and for ensuring the regularity of financial transactions. The Director General and the Chairman of the Health and Safety Commission are jointly responsible for the preparation of the other contents of the Annual Report. My responsibilities, as independent auditor, are guided by the Auditing Practices Board and the auditing profession's ethical guidance.

I report my opinion as to whether the financial statements give a true and fair view and are properly prepared in accordance with the Health and Safety at Work etc Act 1974 and directions made thereunder by the Secretary of State, and whether in all material respects the expenditure and income have been applied to the purposes intended by Parliament and the financial transactions conform to the authorities which govern them. I also report if, in my opinion, the Foreword is not consistent with the financial statements, if the Executive has not kept proper accounting records, or if I have not received all the information and explanations I require for my audit.

I read the other information contained in the Annual Report and consider whether it is consistent with the audited financial statements. I consider the implications for my certificate if I become aware of any apparent misstatements or material inconsistencies with the financial statements.

I review whether the joint statement on pages 123 and 124 reflects the Executive's compliance with Treasury's guidance 'Corporate governance: statement on the system of internal financial control'. I report if it does not meet the requirements specified by Treasury, or if the statement is misleading or inconsistent with other information I am aware of from my audit of the financial statements.

Basis of opinion

I conducted my audit in accordance with Auditing Standards issued by the Auditing Practices Board. An audit includes examination, on a test basis, of evidence relevant to the amounts, disclosures and regularity of financial transactions included in the financial statements. It also includes an assessment of the significant estimates and judgements made by the Director General in the preparation of the financial statements, and of whether the accounting policies are appropriate to the Executive's circumstances, consistently applied and adequately disclosed.

I planned and performed my audit so as to obtain all the information and explanations which I considered necessary in order to provide me with sufficient evidence to give reasonable assurance that the financial statements are free from material misstatement, whether caused by error, or by fraud or other irregularity and that, in all material respects, the expenditure and income have been applied to the purposes intended by Parliament and the financial transactions conform to the authorities which govern them. In forming my opinion I also evaluated the overall adequacy of the presentation of information in the financial statements.

Opinion

In my opinion:

- the financial statements give a true and fair view of the state of affairs of the Health and Safety Executive at 31 March 1999 and of the deficit, total recognised gains and losses and cash flows for the year ended and have been properly prepared in accordance with the Health and Safety at Work etc Act 1974 and the directions made thereunder by the Secretary of State; and

- in all material respects the expenditure and income have been applied to the purposes intended by Parliament and the financial transactions conform to the authorities which govern them.

I have no observations to make on these financial statements.

John Bourn
Comptroller and Auditor General
National Audit Office
157-197 Buckingham Palace Road
London SW1W 9SP

15 October 1999

Health and Safety Executive: Income and Expenditure Account for the year ended 31 March 1999

	Notes	£'000	£'000	Restated 1997/98 £'000
Gross income				
Grant in aid:				
Received from Health and Safety Commission	1e and 17	176 952		178 090
Transfer to deferred government grant account	1e, 17 & Schedule 5	(9 360)		(7 442)
Income from activities:				
Fees and charges	2	25 673		25 131
Sales and other receipts	2	8 434		8 071
EU income		828		-
			202 527	203 850
Surrenders to Consolidated Fund	3		(24)	(1 987)
Change in stocks and in work-in-progress	1i		524	174
Annual release from deferred government grant account	1e, 15 & Schedule 5		12 664	12 083
			215 691	214 120
Expenditure				
Staff costs	5	119 633		117 762
Other operating charges	4	85 918		85 854
Depreciation	1g & 4	10 133		7 628
Deficit on revaluation	1f, 1h	1 681		465
			217 365	211 709
Operating Surplus/(Deficit)			(1 674)	2 411
Loss on disposal of fixed assets			(183)	(75)
Interest on Capital	1n		(2 328)	(2 532)
Surplus/(Deficit) on Ordinary Activities			(4 185)	(196)
Interest on Capital Reversal			2 328	2 159
Surplus/(Deficit) for the financial year	Schedule 5		(1 857)	1 963

The 1997/98 other operating charges and subsequent totals have been restated to reflect the removal of the Notional Insurance in accordance with FRS12, refer note 1m.

All operations were continuing operations throughout 1998/99 and there were no material acquisitions or disposals in the year.

The notes on pages 140 to 158 form part of these financial statements.

Health and Safety Executive: Balance Sheet as at 31 March 1999

	Notes	£'000	£'000	Restated 1997/98 £'000
Fixed assets				
Tangible assets	7		**33 117**	35 942
Current assets				
Stocks	1i & 8	**2 206**		2 056
Debtors	9	**8 686**		9 979
Cash at bank and in hand	10	**1 135**		3 262
		12 027		15 297
Creditors				
Amounts falling due within one year	11	**(7 663)**		(9 036)
Net current assets			**4 364**	6 261
Creditors falling due after more than one year	11	**(52)**		(31)
Provisions for liabilities and charges	12	**(3 005)**	**(3 057)**	(3 000)
Net Assets			**34 424**	39 172
Financed by:				
Capital and reserves				
Deferred government grants	1e & Schedule 5		**49 372**	52 676
General Fund	Schedule 5		**(18 788)**	(17 150)
Revaluation Reserve	1h & Schedule 5		**1 780**	1 724
Current replacement cost reserve	1h & Schedule 5		**2 060**	1 922
Total Government Funds			**34 424**	39 172

The 1997/98 Reserves have been restated to reflect the removal of Notional Insurance in accordance with FRS12, refer Schedule 5 and note 1m.

The notes on pages 140 to 158 form part of these financial statements.

Jenny Bacon CB
Director General, Health and Safety Executive
Accounting Officer   29 September 1999

Health and Safety Executive: Cash Flow Statement for the year ended 31 March 1999

	Notes	£'000	£'000	Restated 1997/98 £'000
Grant in Aid received		176 952		178 090
Other operating cash flows		(179 681)		(177 198)
Net cash inflow/(outflow) from operating activities	15		(2 729)	892
Servicing of finance	1n	-		(373)
Capital expenditure:				
Payments to acquire tangible fixed assets		(9 394)		(7 053)
Receipts from sales of tangible fixed assets		636		396
Net cash outflow from investing activities			(8 758)	(6 657)
Net cash outflow from operating and investing activities:			(11 487)	(6 138)
Financing:				
Government capital grants received	17		9 360	7 442
Increase/(decrease) in cash in the period	15		(2 127)	1 304

The Executive has no debt and no funds or liquid resources other than cash.

The notes of pages 140 to 158 form part of these financial statements.

Health and Safety Executive: Statement of Total Recognised Gains and Losses for the year ended 31 March 1999

	£'000	Restated 1997/98 £'000
Surplus/(deficit) for the year	**(1 857)**	1 963
Unrealised gain on revaluation of land and buildings	**108**	109
Unrealised (loss) on revaluation of other fixed assets	**(1 278)**	(76)
Total gains/(losses) recognised in year	**(3 027)**	1 996
Prior Year Adjustment for Notional Insurance	**(472)**	-
Total gains/(losses) recognised since last annual report	**(3 499)**	**1 996**

The notes on pages 140 to 158 form part of these financial statements.

Health and Safety Executive: Reconciliation of Movements in Government Funds for the year ended 31 March 1999

	£'000	£'000	Restated 1997/98 £'000
Surplus/(Deficit) for the year		(1 857)	1 963
Gain on revaluation of Land and buildings	108		109
Release from Land and Building Reserve	(52)		(52)
Loss on revaluation of other fixed assets	(1 278)		(76)
Release (from)/to CRC Reserve	1 416		(1 800)
Release to General Fund	219		2 289
Net (deduction from)/deferred government grant	(3 304)		(4 641)
		(2 891)	(4 171)
Balance brought forward		39 172	41 380
Balance at 31 March 1999		34 424	39 172

RESERVES

	Deferred government grant £'000	Land & building revaluation reserve £'000	Current replacement cost reserve £'000	Insurance Provision £'000	General Fund £'000	Total £'000
Balance at 1 April 1998	52 676	1 724	1 922	2 500	(19 650)	39 172
Prior year adjustment for notional insurance	-	-	-	(2 500)	2 500	-
Restated Balance at 1 April 1998	52 676	1 724	1 922	-	(17 150)	39 172
Transfer from General Fund	-	-	-		(1 857)	(1 857)
Gain/(Loss) on revaluation	-	108	(1 278)		-	(1 170)
Funds for purchase of fixed assets	9 360	-	-		-	9 360
Release (to)/from General Fund	(12 664)	(52)	1 416		219	(11 081)
Balance at 31 March 1999	49 372	1 780	2 060	-	(18 788)	34 424

The notes on pages 140 to 158 form part of these financial statements.

HEALTH AND SAFETY EXECUTIVE: NOTES TO THE ACCOUNTS

1   Accounting policies

(a)   Accounts Direction

In accordance with Accounts Directions issued by the Secretary of State with the approval of the Treasury the Health and Safety Commission and Health and Safety Executive have prepared a joint Foreword and separate Income and Expenditure Accounts. The Executive has prepared the Balance Sheet (Schedule 2), the Cash Flow Statement (Schedule 3), the Statement of Total Recognised Gains and Losses for the year (Schedule 4) and the Reconciliation of Movements in Government Funds (Schedule 5).

(b)   Accounting Convention

The financial statements are prepared under the historical cost convention modified to include the professional revaluation of land and buildings (including the depreciated replacement cost of the specialist laboratory site at Buxton) and the current replacement cost of other fixed assets and stating stock at the lower of replacement cost and net realisable value.

Without limiting the information given, the accounts meet the accounting and disclosure requirements of the Companies Acts and accounting standards issued or adopted by the Accounting Standards Board, the accounting policies contained in the Resource Accounting Manual and other accounting disclosure requirements issued by HM Treasury from time to time, in so far as those requirements are appropriate.

Following the introduction of Financial Reporting Standard 12, the treatment of insurance has changed, refer para 1(m) and the Accounts Direction for details.

(c)   Current replacement cost accounting

The modified historical cost financial statements have been prepared in accordance with the principles set out in the Accounting Standards Committee publication 'Accounting for the effects of Inflation: A Handbook' and guidance from the Treasury.

The current replacement cost system does not account for general inflation but allows for price changes, which affect the Executive, when reporting details of fixed assets and the operating result.

(d)   Analysis of activities

All the activities of the Executive are designed to use the measures in the Health and Safety at Work etc Act 1974 to further the reduction of occupational accidents and disease. The Executive, under the Accounts Direction issued by the Secretary of State has not provided for an analysis of costs and related revenues by each separate activity.

140

(e)   Government grants

Pursuant to Section 43 of the Health and Safety at Work etc Act 1974, the Commission is financed by a grant in aid borne on a Vote of the Department of the Environment, Transport and the Regions (Class V1 Vote 5), details of which are contained in Note 17.

The Commission pays to the Executive such sums as the Commission considers appropriate for the purpose of enabling the Executive to perform its functions. The grant in aid is credited to income in the year to which it relates, excluding that which relates to capital acquisitions which is credited to a deferred government grant account a proportion of which is released to the Income and Expenditure Account annually over the lives of the assets to which it relates.

(f)   Assets

All assets are held by the Health and Safety Executive on behalf of the Health and Safety Commission.

Items of equipment costing less than £2000, are charged to expenditure in the year of purchase, except for computer equipment costing over £500 but less than £2000 and items of furniture costing less than £2000 which are grouped for capitalisation by year of acquisition.

Items of equipment purchased under research contracts and held by outside bodies are charged to expenditure in the year of purchase.

Fixed assets are capitalised at cost of acquisition and installation.

Land and buildings are valued at open market value in existing use except for the specialist laboratory site at Buxton which has been included at depreciated replacement cost.

In accordance with recent HM Treasury guidance valuations will be undertaken every five years or less. Only the values of freeholds and leaseholds with a rent review period of more than seven years have been included in the Balance Sheet, in line with current Treasury guidance.

(g)   Depreciation

Freehold land is not depreciated.

Depreciation is provided on all other tangible fixed assets from the date of acquisition or from the date of revaluation in the case of buildings and leasehold land.

Depreciation is calculated to write-off the replacement cost or valuation of an asset evenly over its expected useful life except for vehicles acquired for the car leasing scheme where 60 per cent of the original cost is depreciated over the three year life of the contract.

It is impractical to calculate average asset lives exactly, however the initial periods over which depreciation is applied to major assets are:-

141

Buildings:	freehold	over 50 years or remaining life assessed by the valuers
	leasehold	over period of lease or to next rent review
Specialist plant		over remaining life
Furniture		up to 15 years
Office machinery, publicity & major scientific equipment		up to 10 years
Printing/typesetting and telecommunications equipment, computers and vehicles		up to 7 years
Micro computers		up to 5 years
Cars leased to staff		up to 3 years

The economic life of a number of asset categories have been reduced during the year. There has been a one off charge to depreciation of £2 200 000 as a result of these changes in respect of assets now fully depreciated. The overall impact on the depreciation charge for 1998/99 was £2 600 000.

(h)   Revaluation reserves

Surpluses arising on the revaluation of land and buildings are credited to a revaluation reserve. Increases between the current net replacement cost and historic net book value for other fixed assets are charged to a current replacement cost reserve. Deficits are charged to these reserves in respect of amounts previously credited; the balance of any deficit is debited to the General Fund.

The current replacement cost depreciation adjustment provides for the difference between the value to the Executive of fixed assets consumed in the year and the depreciation charged on an historical cost basis. In line with the accounting policies contained in the Resource Accounting Manual, the adjustment has been taken direct to Reserves (refer Schedule 5) rather than the General Fund.

(i)   Stocks

Stocks of priced publications and consumables held by the Executive are stated at the lower of replacement cost or net realisable value after provision for obsolescence. The costs incurred on work-in-progress and finished goods in bringing each publication to its present location and condition are the cost of direct materials and labour plus attributable overheads on normal levels of activity.

Net realisable value is based on the estimated selling prices, less further costs expected to be incurred to completion and disposal.

142

(j)   Foreign currency

Assets and liabilities denominated in foreign currencies are translated into sterling at the exchange rates prevailing at the year-end.

All other gains and losses are dealt with through the Income and Expenditure Account.

(k)   Repair and renewals

Expenditure on repairs, renewals and minor items of equipment is charged to expenditure in the year to which it relates.

(l)   Research

Expenditure on research is written off in the year in which it was incurred.

(m)   Notional insurance reserve

Following the publication of FRS 12, apart from commercial insurance premiums relating to leased vehicles and foreign travel, it is only expenditure in connection with uninsured risks that are charged to the income and expenditure account and the corresponding amount has been adjusted accordingly. The balance on the Insurance Reserve (refer Schedule 5) has been transferred to the General Fund. The 1997/98 other operating charges and subsequent totals within the Income and Expenditure Account (refer Schedule 1) have been adjusted by £472 086 to reflect this.

(n)   Notional interest on capital

Notional interest has been charged on fixed assets and working capital at the 6.0% rate prescribed by Treasury and is reversed after the line showing deficit on ordinary activities. An Opportunity Cost Rental of £552 000 was paid in 1997/98 to PACE by HSL of which £373 000 is considered to represent a capital charge of 6% of the land and building value and the reversal has been adjusted accordingly.

(o)   Pension costs

The employees of the Health and Safety Executive are Civil Servants to whom the conditions of the Superannuation Acts 1965 and 1972 and subsequent amendments apply. The staff are covered by the Principal Civil Service Pension Scheme (PCSPS) which is a non-contributory scheme. The rate of the employer's contribution is determined from time to time by the Government Actuary and advised by the Treasury and is charged to the Income and Expenditure Account.

In addition, the Health and Safety Executive operates an Early Retirement Scheme which gives retirement benefits to certain qualifying employees. These benefits conform to the rules of the PCSPS. The Health and Safety Executive bears the costs of these benefits until the normal retiring age of the employees retired under the Early Retirement Scheme.

The total pensions liability up to retiring age of each employee is charged to the Income and Expenditure Account in the year in which the employee takes early retirement.

(p)   Operating Leases

The costs of operating leases in respect of Land and Buildings and equipment are charged to expenditure in the year to which they relate.

2   Income

The activities of the Executive include certain chargeable and statutory services each of which is subject to a financial objective of full cost recovery and for which a Memorandum Trading Account is prepared. The charges for these activities, which are exclusive of VAT, include provision for the recovery of notional interest, apart from the licensing of nuclear installations where the notional charge is not an expense that can be recovered under the Nuclear Installations Act 1965.

The Health and Safety Laboratory (HSL) became an in-house agency of HSE on 1 April 1995 and operates on 'Next Steps Agency' principles under the direction of a Chief Executive, who is also their accounting officer. They are required to recover the full economic cost of their operations in accordance with HM Treasury's Fees and Charges guidance and are subject to the controls imposed on a net running costs regime. HSEs income and expenditure includes that for the Laboratory.

	Cost	Income	Surplus/ (Deficit)	Surplus/ (Deficit)
				1997/98
	£'000	£'000	£'000	£'000
(i) HSE fees and charges				
Licensing of nuclear installations	17 074	17 074	-	-
Safety related research in the nuclear industry	1 570	1 570	-	-
Sponsored Conferences	359	254	(105)	-
Electrical Equipment Certification Unit	2 509	2 532	23	(58)
Asbestos Licensing Unit	188	124	(64)	(123)
Approval of non-agricultural pesticides	1 821	1 821	-	-
Notification of New Substances	491	415	(76)	(91)
	24 012	23 790	(222)	(272)
Health and Safety Laboratory External Customers	1 514	1 679	165	
Other Fees & Agency Charges	-	204		
Total Fees & Charges at 31 March 1999	**25 526**	**25 673**		
Total Fees & Charges at 31 March 1998	24 270	25 131		
(ii) HSE Sales & other receipts				
Sale of publications	4 128	5 092	964	1 309
Other sales/income (see note below)	-	3 342	-	-
Total sales & other receipts at 31 March 1999	**4 128**	**8 434**		
Total sales & other receipts at 31 March 1998	3 796	8 071		

This analysis conforms with the HM Treasury's 'The Fees and Charges Guide' and is not intended to comply with SSAP25 Segmental Reporting.

Rents receivable included in other sales/income above, is as follows:

		1997/98
	£'000	£'000
Rent from Department of Environment, Transport and the Regions	-	-
Rents from other Government Departments	**58**	44
Rents from external tenants	**51**	18

3   Surrenders to Consolidated Fund

	£'000	1997/98 £'000
Surrender of windfall receipts	24	23
Surrender of excess working balance	-	1 964
	24	1 987

The sum of £24 067 was surrendered to the Exchequer as a Consolidated Fund extra receipt.

4   Operating surplus/deficit of the Health and Safety Executive

This is stated after charging as expenditure:

	£'000	1997/98 £'000
Staff costs (see Note 5)	119 633	117 762
General administrative expenses	22 472	21 880
Travel, subsistence and hospitality of staff (see note below)	10 890	9 794
Rates, maintenance & other premises costs	14 261	13 965
Other operating lease rentals	8 337	11 218
Research, testing & survey services	15 106	17 351
Other current expenditure on goods and services	14 090	11 341
External Audit fees	71	111
Provision for bad debts & general losses (see note over)	691	193
Fixed asset adjustment	-	1
Depreciation (see Note 7)	10 139	7 634
Depreciation Release - Carlisle	(6)	(6)
Deficit on revaluation	1 681	465
	217 365	211 709

Note: Travel, subsistence and hospitality expenses for the Executive Members was £24 553 (1997/98 - £22 037), whilst the total for all other staff was £10 863 608   (1997/98 - £9 772 361).

The provision for bad debts and general losses figure of £691 812 includes:-

			1997/98
		£'000	£'000
(a)	Provision for bad debts	421	(32)
(b)	Stock losses including provision	148	136
(c)	General losses	101	89
(d)	Special payments	21	-
		691	193

5   Staff costs of the Health and Safety Executive

	£'000	£'000
Wages and salaries	96 940	94 559
Social Security costs	7 651	7 369
Superannuation costs	15 042	15 834
	119 633	117 762

Emoluments of Director General

	Salary	Pension Contributions	Other Taxable Benefits	Total	1997/98 Total
	£	£	£	£	£
Jenny Bacon CB	104 269	19 290	-	123 559	117 460

Executive Members Emoluments:

	Notes	Salary	Pension Contributions	Other Taxable Benefits	Total	1997/98 Total
		£	£	£	£	£
David Eves CB		88 837	16 435	-	105 272	99 215
Richard Hillier		80 668	14 923	-	95 591	89 698
		169 505	31 358	-	200 863	188 913

Notes:

The Executive are all members of the Principal Civil Service Pension Scheme (PCSPS).

Other taxable benefits of the Director General and the Executive include mileage and offshore allowances. These benefits are taxed at source.

The Executive members are appointed for a fixed term of up to three years. None of the members receive any predetermined annual bonus or predetermined compensation payment on termination of office.

Emoluments of other senior employees falling within the following ranges:

	No.	No.
£40 000 - £49 999	334	380
£50 000 - £59 999	160	103
£60 000 - £69 999	29	28
£70 000 - £79 999	7	1
£80 000 - £89 999	3	-

The average number of employees during the year of the account was made up as follows:

	No.	No.
Inspectors	1 467	1 439
Other Professional /Specialist Staff	1 239	1 228
Non Specialist Staff	1 200	1 337
	3 906	4 004

Full details of the occupational breakdown of staff in post are given in the Annual Report, refer paragraphs 1.167 and 1.168.

6   Related Party Transactions

The Health and Safety Executive is an Executive Non-Departmental Public Body with Crown status and is sponsored by the Department of the Environment, Transport and Regions (DETR).

DETR is regarded as a related party. During the year, HSE did have transactions with DETR which mainly related to the provision of premises and research services. HSC and HSE did not have material transactions with other entities for which the DETR is regarded as the parent Department.

In addition, HSE had a number of material transactions with other Government Departments and other central government bodies. The significant transactions have been with the Benefits Agency (expenditure £487 000, 1997/98 - £590 000), Central Office of Information (£594 000, 1997/98 - £579 000), Civil Service College (£287 000, 1997/98 - £268 000), Defence Evaluation Research Agency (£153 000, 1997/98 - £201 000), Department of Health (£266 000, 1997/98 - £146 000) and Ministry of Agriculture, Fisheries and Food (expenditure £203 000, 1997/98 - £197 000 and income of £1 821 000, 1997/98 - £1 672 000), and mainly relate to premises, research, training, computer and administrative expenditure together with relevant income from the provision of health and safety advice and services.

HSE also had a number of transactions with Other Government Departments but which are not considered material.

None of the Executive members or key management staff or any persons connected with them have any interest in any material transactions undertaken by HSC/HSE during the year.

7   Tangible fixed assets

Fixed asset values	Land & buildings £'000	Machinery, equipment computers & plant £'000	Vehicles, furniture & office machines £'000	Total £'000
Cost or valuation at 1 April 1998	8 055	36 658	16 265	60 978
Adjustments	-	-	-	-
Additions in year	375	6 856	2 163	9 394
Revaluations in year	116	(3 291)	100	(3 075)
Disposals during year	-	(9 018)	(3 827)	(12 845)
Balance at 31 March 1999	8 546	31 205	14 701	54 452
Depreciation: at 1 April 1998	561	17 923	6 552	25 036
Charge in year:				
Historical	820	8 812	2 093	11 725
Supplementary	(478)	(1 296)	188	(1 586)
Charge in year	342	7 516	2 281	10 139
Backlog	7	(1 906)	46	(1 853)
On revaluations in year	-	(62)	-	(62)
Disposals during year	-	(8 679)	(3 246)	(11 925)
Accumulated Depreciation at 31 March 1999	910	14 792	5 633	21 335
Net current replacement Cost at 31 March 1999	7 636	16 413	9 068	33 117
Net current replacement Cost at 31 March 1998	7 494	18 735	9 713	35 942

Details of property valuations are contained in the Foreword, note 4 and are as follows:

		Current valuation
Land		
		£'000
Freehold:	Sheffield	350
	Buxton	325
	Sheffield Royal Exchange	50
Leasehold:	Sheffield	50
	Stoneleigh	-
Buildings		
Freehold:	Sheffield Royal Exchange	200
	Sheffield Laboratory	4 200
	Buxton	1 250
Leasehold:	St Hugh's House, Bootle	770
	Stoneleigh	53
	Carlisle	184
		7 432

Note: The leasehold property at Sheffield, Broad Lane was revalued with a negative value of £3 000 000. A dilapidation provision for this amount has been established to meet the cost of the lease obligations.

Land and buildings

The net book value at 31 March 1999 of land and buildings comprises:

	£'000	1997/98 £'000
Freehold	6 113	6 176
Long Leasehold	387	401
Short Leasehold	1 136	917
	7 636	**7 494**

Historical costs

The historical cost and depreciation of land and buildings included at valuation and other assets included at net current replacement value is as follows:

	Land & buildings	Machinery, equipment computers & plant	Vehicles, furniture & office machines	Total
	£'000	£'000	£'000	£'000
Net book value at 1 April 1998	23 519	19 779	9 378	52 676
Additions in year	376	6 822	2 162	9 360
Valuations	-	-	-	-
Disposals	-	(13 309)	(3 082)	(16 391)
Adjustment	-	-	-	-
Depreciation in year	(820)	(8 821)	(2 094)	(11 735)
Disposals	-	12 957	2 505	15 462
Net book value at 31 March 1999	23 075	17 428	8 869	49 372

8 Stocks

		1997/98
	£'000	£'000
Consumables	126	255
Work-in-progress	562	236
Finished stock for sale	1 518	1 565
	2 206	2 056

9 Debtors

	£'000	1997/98 £'000
Debts falling due within one year:		
Trade debtors	839	3 128
Less provision for bad debts	(418)	(418)
Imprests/advances	826	942
Prepayments	2 504	2 952
Taxation: VAT debtor	1 966	2 399
Other debtors	4	-
Accrued income	2 009	-
	7 730	9 003
Debts falling due after more than one year:		
Imprests/advances	956	976
Total	8 686	9 979

A new presentation for the analysis of debtors has been adopted. The comparative data is not available but it should be noted that there is no change to the overall total value.

The imprests/advances total of £1 782 094 (1997/98 - £1 918 002) includes £904 060 (1997/98 - £1 249 115) advances of salary for house purchase, £275 613 (1997/98 - £257 798) advances of salary for season ticket purchase, and £202 094 (1997/98 - £199 433) imprests.

There were 157 officers who had £2500 or more outstanding at 31 March 1999 which totalled £1 196 941 (1997/98 - £1 231 518 relating to 161 officers).

10 Cash

		£'000	1997/98 £'000
Cash:	with Paymaster General	1 036	3 191
	at bank and in hand	99	71
		1 135	3 262

11 Creditors

	£'000	1997/98 £'000
Amounts falling due within one year:		
Trade creditors	268	8 265
Other creditors	1 326	-
Payments on account	1 483	771
Accruals	4 586	-
	7 663	9 036

	£'000	1997/98 £'000
Amounts falling due after more than one year:		
Other creditors	52	-
Payments received on account	-	31
	52	31

A new presentation for the analysis of creditors and accruals has been adopted. The comparative data is not available but it should be noted that there is no change to the overall total value.

12 Provision for Liabilities and Charges

	£'000	1997/98 £'000
Sheffield site dilapidation costs	3 000	3 000
Insurance claim	5	-
	3 005	3 000

154

13 Operating Lease Commitments

Lease rentals payable in next financial year for equipment and buildings occupied by the Executive.

Leases expiring within:

| | Land and Building £'000 | Other £'000 | 1997/98 | |
			Land and Building £'000	Other £'000
One year	92	14	416	-
Two to five years	2 764	91	2 507	58
More than 5 years	4 861	-	5 028	-
	7 717	105	7 951	58

14 Superannuation

For 1998/99 the rates of superannuation for non-industrial staff apply according to grade at 12%, 13.5%, 16.5% and 18.5%.

For 1998/99 contributions of £14 240 006 were paid over to the Office of HM Paymaster General (1997/98 contributions totalled £13 534 391).

In addition, the Health and Safety Executive operates an Early Retirement Scheme which gives retirement benefits to certain qualifying employees. These benefits conform to the rules of the PCSPS.

The total pensions liability up to retiring age of each employee is charged to the Income and Expenditure account in the year in which the employee takes early retirement. For 1998/99 these costs amounted to £802 426 (1997/98 costs were £2 406 572).

155

15   Cash Flow Statement

	Notes	£'000	Restated 1997/98 £'000
Reconciliation of operating surplus/(deficit) to net cash outflow from operating activities			
Operating surplus/(deficit) for year	Schedule 1	**(1 674)**	2 411
Depreciation charge	4	**10 139**	7 634
Fixed asset adjustment	4	**-**	1
Depreciation release - Carlisle	4	**(6)**	(6)
Release from deferred government grant	Schedule 5	**(12 664)**	(12 086)
Deficit on revaluation of fixed assets		**1 681**	465
(Increase)/Decrease in stock	8	**(150)**	-
Decrease/(Increase) in debtors		**1 293**	5
Increase/(Decrease) in creditors		**(1 353)**	2 468
Increase in provisions		**5**	-
Net cash inflow/(outflow) from operating activities	Schedule 3	**(2 729)**	892
Reconciliation of movement in cash to movement in net funds:			
Increase/(decrease) in cash in the period	Schedule 3	**(2 127)**	1 304
Net funds at 1 April 1998		**3 262**	1 958
Net funds at 31 March 1999	10	**1 135**	3 262

Analysis of net funds	As at 1 April 1998	Cash Flow in year	As at 31 March 1999
Cash at bank and in hand:	**3 262**	**(2 127)**	**1 135**

16   Capital commitments

	£'000	1997/98 £'000
Contracted	**331**	1 034

17   Grant in aid

Pursuant to Section 43 of the Health and Safety at Work etc Act 1974, the Commission is financed by a grant in aid borne on a Vote of the Department of the Environment, Transport and the Regions (Class VI Vote 5).

The total grant in aid received by the Health and Safety Executive from the Health and Safety Commission was £176 952 488 of which £9 360 079 was in respect of capital acquisitions and was credited to a deferred government grant account while the balance of £167 592 409 was credited as income in the year.

18   Working balance at 31 March 1998

The actual unspent issues of grant in aid at 31 March 1999 were £2 340 251. The Health and Safety Executive, acting on behalf of the Commission, is authorised by the Treasury to retain unspent issues of grant in aid to a maximum of 2% of the grant.

19 Statement of cash expenditure and provision

	1998/99 (provision)	1998/99 (outturn)	1997/98 (outturn)
Current expenditure	£'000	£'000	£'000
Running costs	164 085	163 896	161 277
Other current expenditure	48 331	48 061	49 767
Current sub-total	212 416	211 957	211 044
Capital expenditure			
Capital equipment	6 695	8 176	6 915
Capital building	755	45	83
Capital sub-total	7 450	8 221	6 998
Health and Safety Laboratory	1 444	(2 499)	(1 990)
Receipts - Fees and charges	(36 722)	(36 297)	(36 982)
- Recovered VAT	(2 360)	(2 605)	(2 463)
Total receipts	(39 082)	(38 902)	(39 445)
Grand Total: Net	182 228	178 777	176 607
gross	221 310	217 679	216 052

Notes:

1. The figures include HSC expenditure.

2. The total grant in aid drawn down in 1998/99 was £177.5 million (refer HSC I & E Account) differing from the grand total net figure by £1.3 million, representing a decrease in the working balance.

As regards the financial target established with the Department of the Environment, Transport and the Regions in respect of spending within cash provision, HSE achieved net expenditure within 1% of the agreed total.

THE HEALTH & SAFETY COMMISSION : ACCOUNTS DIRECTION

The Secretary of State for the Environment, Transport and the Regions with the approval of the Treasury and in accordance with paragraph 14(1) of Schedule 2 to the Health and Safety at Work etc Act 1974, hereby notifies the Health and Safety Commission (hereafter in this direction referred to as 'the Commission') of the following requirements in respect of its annual accounts.

1   The annual accounts, which it is the duty of the Commission to prepare in respect of each financial year, shall comprise:

    (a)   a foreword;

    (b)   an income and expenditure account; and

    (c)   a balance sheet

    including in each case such notes and additional information as may be necessary for the purposes referred to in paragraph 2 below and in Schedule 2 to this direction.

2   The annual accounts shall give a true and fair view of the income and expenditure of the Commission and the state of affairs at the year end. Subject to this requirement, the annual accounts shall be prepared in accordance with:

    (a)   the accounting and disclosure requirements of the Companies Act 1985;

    (b)   generally accepted accounting practice in the United Kingdom;

    (c)   the accounting and disclosure requirements given in *Government Accounting* and in the Treasury guidance *Executive Non-Departmental Public Bodies Annual Reports and Accounts Guidance*, as amended or augmented from time to time; and

    (d)   any other guidance that the Treasury may issue from time to time in respect of accounts that are required to give a true and fair view;

    insofar as these requirements are appropriate to the Commission and are in force for the year for which the accounts are prepared.

3   Clarification of the application of the accounting and disclosure requirements of the Companies Act 1985 and accounting standards is given in Schedule 1 to this direction. Additional disclosures required by the Secretary of State for the Environment, Transport and the Regions are set out in Schedule 2.

4   This direction shall be reproduced as an appendix to the annual accounts.

159

5   This direction replaces that dated 11 June 1997.

Signed by the authority of the Secretary

of State for the Environment, Transport and the Regions

S A Williams

An officer in the
Department of the Environment, Transport and
the Regions

Date   *27 March 1998*

Application of the Accounting and Disclosure Requirements of the Companies Act 1985, Accounting Standards and Generally Accepted Accounting Practice

1   Disclosure exemptions for small and medium-sized companies permitted by the Companies Act 1985 or by accounting standards shall not apply to the Commission with the exception of the disclosure exemption concerning cash flow statements.

2   The foreword shall contain the information required to be disclosed in directors' reports attached to companies' annual accounts, to the extent that such requirements are appropriate to the Commission and for which purpose members of the Commission and the accounting officer shall be taken to be directors.

3   If there are no material amounts that would otherwise need to be disclosed as balances in a primary statement, this fact may be shown in a note to the annual accounts instead of in a balance sheet.

4   The annual accounts shall be signed and dated on behalf of the Commission's board members by its accounting officer.

Additional Disclosure Requirements

The following information shall be disclosed in the annual accounts, as a minimum, and in addition to the information required to be disclosed by paragraphs 1 and 2 of this direction.

1   **The foreword**

   (a)   a description of the Commission's history and background

   (b)   a statement that the annual accounts have been prepared in a form directed by the Secretary of State with the approval of the Treasury in accordance with paragraph 14(1) of Schedule 2 to the Health and Safety at Work etc Act 1974.

2   **The income and expenditure account, or the notes thereto**

   (a)   the following income -

      (i)   grant-in-aid; and

   (b)   the following expenditure -

      (i)   the amount payable to the Health and Safety Executive; and

      (ii)   administrative expenditure.

3   **The notes to the annual accounts**

   (a)   a report on the emoluments of members of the Commission and the emoluments of the accounting officer during the year, with separate disclosure where more than one person occupied these offices. The report shall include full details of all elements in the remuneration package of each person by name, such as fees, salary, annual bonuses, payments on termination of office, pension contributions, and the performance related elements of these (for which the basis on which the performance is measured shall be explained). If a member of the Commission has been appointed for a fixed term or if the accounting officer is on a fixed term service contract, the term shall be stated together with details of any predetermined compensation on termination of office;

   (b)   a statement on the pension arrangements for members of the Commission and for the accounting officer, as follows:

      (i)   if they are members of the ordinary pension scheme, this shall be stated;

      (ii)   if they are members of the ordinary scheme but with additional or enhanced contributions made by the Commission, the amounts of all the contributions shall be shown; and

(iii)   if the Commission has made any contributions to a personal pension plan, the amount shall be stated;

(c)   a statement on employees, other than members of the Commission, showing:

    (i)   the number of employees during the year whose emoluments (excluding pension contributions but including the other elements mentioned in paragraph 3(a), above), fell in each bracket of a scale in multiples of £10 000 per annum, starting at £40 000 per annum;

    (ii)   the average number of persons employed during the year, including part-time employees, analysed between appropriate categories; and

    (iii)   employee costs during the year, showing separately:

        (1)   wages and salaries;

        (2)   social security costs; and

        (3)   other pension costs, with details;

(d)   particulars of any transaction, arrangement or contract (other than a contract of service or of employment with the Commission), including transactions at arm's length, entered into by the Commission with another party, exceeding £5 000 in value, in which a member of the Commission, the accounting officer, a senior employee, or a person connected with any of the foregoing (a close family member, a member of the same household, a dependent relative or a business partner), at any time during the year, had a direct or indirect financial interest that was notified to the Commission (except an interest that arises only as a consequence of an indirect interest in a contract etc entered into by a third party with the Commission). For these purposes, financial interest includes directorships; and senior employee means a person who is a member of the Senior Civil Service.

(e)   a statement of the total expenses payable for the year to members of the Commission and employees respectively - expenses being reimbursements and other expenditure in respect of travelling, subsistence and hospitality; and

163

(f)   a statement of losses and special payments during the year, being transactions of a type which Parliament cannot be supposed to have contemplated. Disclosure shall be made of the total of losses and special payments if this exceeds £100 000, with separate disclosure and particulars of any individual amounts in excess of £100 000. Disclosure shall also be made of any loss or special payment of £100 000 and below if it is considered material in the context of the Commission's operations.

4   In this schedule, grant-in-aid means grants made to the Commission by the Secretary of State pursuant to section 43(1) of the Health and Safety at Work etc Act 1974.

THE HEALTH & SAFETY EXECUTIVE : ACCOUNTS DIRECTION

The Secretary of State for the Environment, Transport and Regions with the approval of the Treasury and in accordance with paragraph 20 of Schedule 2 to the Health and Safety at Work etc Act 1974, hereby notifies the Health and Safety Executive (hereafter in this direction referred to as 'the Executive') of the following requirements in respect of its annual accounts.

1   The annual accounts, which it is the duty of the Executive to prepare in respect of each financial year, shall comprise:

    (a)   a foreword;

    (b)   an income and expenditure account;

    (c)   a statement of total recognised gains and losses, where applicable;

    (d)   a balance sheet; and

    (e)   a cash flow statement

including in each case such notes and additional information as may be necessary for the purposes referred to in paragraph 2, below, and in Schedule 2 to this direction.

2   The annual accounts shall give a true and fair view of the income and expenditure and cash flows for the year and the state of affairs at the year end. Subject to this requirement, the annual accounts shall be prepared in accordance with:

    (a)   the accounting and disclosure requirements of the Companies Act 1985;

    (b)   generally accepted accounting practice in the United Kingdom;

    (c)   the accounting and disclosure requirements given in *The Fees and Charges Guide* in particular those relating to the need for segmental information for services or forms of services provided by the Executive;

    (d)   the accounting and disclosure requirements given in *Government Accounting* and in the Treasury guidance *Executive Non-Departmental Public Bodies Annual Reports and Accounts Guidance*, as amended or augmented from time to time; and

    (e)   any other guidance that the Treasury may issue from time to time in respect of accounts that are required to give a true and fair view;

insofar as these requirements are appropriate to the Executive and are in force for the year for which the accounts are prepared.

3   Clarification of the application of the accounting and disclosure requirements of the Companies Act 1985 and accounting standards is given in Schedule 1 to this direction. Additional disclosures required by the Secretary of State for the Environment, Transport and the Regions are set out in Schedule 2.

4   This direction shall be reproduced as an appendix to the annual accounts.

5   This direction replaces that dated 11 June 1997.

Signed by authority of the Secretary

of State for the Environment, Transport and the Regions

S A Williams

An officer in the
Department of the Environment, Transport and the Regions
_____

Date   *27 March 1998*

and as amended on 24 August 1999
_____

Application of the Accounting and Disclosure Requirements of the Companies Act 1985, Accounting Standards and Generally Accepted Accounting Practice

1   Disclosure exemptions for small and medium-sized companies permitted by the Companies Act 1985 or by accounting standards shall not apply to the Executive.

2   The foreword shall contain the information required to be disclosed in directors' reports attached to companies' annual accounts, to the extent that such requirements are appropriate to the Executive and for which purpose members of the Executive and the accounting officer shall be taken to be directors.

3   The Executive's income and expenditure account shall be in format 2 as set out in Schedule 4 to the Companies Act 1985, adapted where necessary to suit the special nature of the Executive's business. The balance sheet shall be in format 1 as set out in Schedule 4 to the Companies Act 1985.

4   Operating costs in the income and expenditure account shall include a notional cost of capital, at 6% of the average of total assets less current liabilities, to the extent that there is no real charge for this. This amount shall be disclosed separately and shall be reversed after the line showing the surplus or deficit for the year.

5   The requirement of accounting standard FRS3 to include a note of the historical cost profit or loss for the year where this amount is materially different from the result shown in the income and expenditure account, shall not apply to the Executive.

6   Except where the Treasury has agreed otherwise, freehold land and non-leased buildings held as fixed assets shall be stated at existing use value or, for property of a specialised nature, at depreciated replacement cost. Other non-leased fixed assets shall be stated at net current replacement cost. All valuation bases as defined by the Royal Institution of Chartered Surveyors.

7   Stocks shall be stated at the lower of replacement cost and net realisable value.

8   The foreword and balance sheet shall be signed and dated on behalf of the Executive's board members by its accounting officer.

Additional Disclosure Requirements

The following information shall be disclosed in the annual accounts, as a minimum, and in addition to the information required to be disclosed by paragraphs 1 and 2 of this direction.

1   **The foreword or a separate statement after the foreword**

   (a)   a statement on corporate governance, similar to the statement required by the London Stock Exchange on compliance with the Code of Best Practice contained in the report by the Committee on The Financial Aspects of Corporate Governance, but adapted for the different circumstances applying to non-departmental public bodies. However, the Executive need not confirm that there has been an annual review of the effectiveness of internal financial controls, nor state that its business is a going concern.

   (b)   a description of the Executive's history and background; and

   (c)   a statement that the annual accounts have been prepared in a form directed by the Secretary of State with the approval of the Treasury, in accordance with paragraph 20 of Schedule 2 to the Health and Safety at Work etc Act 1974.

2   **The income and expenditure account**

   grant-in-aid income for the year.

3   **The balance sheet, or the notes thereto**

   (a)   an analysis of liquid resources (as defined by accounting standard FRS1);

   (b)   prepayments; and

   (c)   accrued income.

4   **The notes to the annual accounts**

   (a)   a statement of performance against key financial targets agreed in advance with the Department of the Environment, Transport and the Regions;

   (b)   a report on the emoluments of members of the Executive and emoluments of the accounting officer during the year (with separate disclosure where more than one person occupied this office). The report shall include full details of all elements in the remuneration package of each person by name or job title, such as fees, salary, annual bonuses, payment on termination of office, other taxable benefits, pension contributions, and the performance related elements of these (for which the basis on which the performance is measured shall be explained). If a member of the Executive has been appointed for a fixed term or if the accounting officer is on a fixed-term service contract, the term shall be stated together with details of any predetermined compensation on termination of office;

(c)   a statement of the pension arrangements for members of the Executive and for the accounting officer, as follows:

   (i)   if they are members of the ordinary pension scheme, this shall be stated

   (ii)   if they are members of the ordinary scheme but with additional or enhanced contributions made by the Executive, the amounts of all such contributions shall be shown

   (iii) if the Executive has made any contributions to a personal pension plan, the amount shall be shown;

(d)   details of employees, other than members of the Executive and the accounting officer, showing:

   (i)   the number of employees during the year whose emoluments (excluding pension contributions but including the other elements mentioned in paragraph 4(b), above), fell in each bracket of a scale in multiples of £10 000 per annum, starting at £40 000 per annum

   (ii)   the average number of persons employed during the year, including part-time employees, analysed between appropriate categories

   (iii) employees costs during the year, showing separately

      (1)   wages and salaries

      (2)   social security costs

      (3)   other pension costs, with details

(e)   particulars of any transaction, arrangement or contract (other than a contract of service or of employment with the Executive), including transactions at arm's length, entered into by the Executive with another party, exceeding £5 000 in value, in which a member of the Executive, an executive, a senior employee, or a person connected with any of the foregoing (a close family member, a member of the same household, a dependent relative, a business partner or a company with which one of the foregoing held a contract of service as a director), at any time during the year, had a direct or indirect financial interest that was notified to the Executive (except an interest that arises only as a consequence of an indirect interest in a contract etc entered into by a third party with the Executive). For these purposes, a senior employee means a person who is a member of the Senior Civil Service;

169

(f)   a statement of the total expenses payable for the year to members of the Executive and employees respectively - expenses being reimbursements and other expenditure in respect of travelling, subsistence and hospitality;

(g)   a statement of losses and special payments during the year, being transactions of a type which Parliament cannot be supposed to have contemplated. Disclosure shall be made of the total of losses and special payments if this exceeds £100 000, with separate disclosure and particulars of any individual amounts in excess of £100 000. Disclosure shall also be made of any loss or special payment of £100 000 and below if it is considered material in the context of the Executive's operations; and

(h)   a statement of cash expenditure and receipts, referring to the appropriate vote and class, and analysed as in the Expected Use of Grant-in-Aid table for the Health and Safety Commission, annexed to *The Department of the Environment, Transport and the Regions' Annual Report on the Government's Expenditure Plans*;

5   In this schedule, grant-in-aid means grant made by the Secretary of State pursuant to section 43(1) of the Health and Safety at Work etc Act 1974 and passed to the Executive by the Health and Safety Commission.

THE HEALTH AND SAFETY EXECUTIVE: *unaudited* RESOURCE ACCOUNTS

The Government is in the process of introducing resource accounting and budgeting which is a major change in the way in which the public sector plans, controls and accounts for expenditure by:-

- focusing more on resources consumed and not just on the cash spent in a particular year

- treating capital and current expenditure in a way which better reflects their economic significance

- encouraging a greater emphasis on outputs and the achievement of aims and objectives.

This in turn will lead to better informed decisions about overall public spending priorities, within the context of the Government's macro economic objectives.

As part of its preparations for the formal introduction of resource accounting and budgeting HSE has produced financial statements which are in the new format. These 'dry run' schedules are *unaudited*, audited schedules will not be required until next year, but are reproduced here for purposes of illustration.

- Schedules 2, 3 and 4 broadly correspond to the private sector's main financial statements

- Schedule 5 links inputs to aims and objectives.

HSE has for some time produced financial statements based on accrual accounting techniques (refer Foreword, paragraph 1) and consistent with the relevant accounting standards etc. These new style schedules are in a number of respects very similar to the current version of the financial statements and the figures in the schedules are consistent with those contained in the statements. The references to 'note' are those contained within the main body of the accounts.

HSC/HSE has achieved the requirements of Stage 1 implementation as laid down by HM Treasury, which means that the methodology for producing these schedules has been accepted in principle. The schedules usefully augment the information contained in Section 2 of the Annual Report and show the link with our operational strategy as outlined in the HSC Plan of Work.

Health and Safety Executive: Operating Cost Statement for the year ended 31 March 1999

	Note	£600	1998/99 £'000	Restated 1997/98 £'000
Administration costs				
Staff costs	4		119 633	117 762
Other Operating Costs			99 719	96 380
Gross Administration Costs			219 352	214 142
Operating income	2		(34 935)	(33 202)
Non-recurring administration costs:				
Release to CRC Reserve			-	-
Net Administration Costs			184 417	180 940
Other adjustments				
Current grant Transfer to Deferred Govt	7	9 360		7 442
Annual Release from Deferred Govt Grant Account		(12 664)		(12 083)
Net adjustments			(3 304)	(4 641)
Net Operating Cost	Schedule 4 & 5		181 113	176 299
Resource Budget Outturn			181 113	176 299

Statement of Recognised Gains and Losses for the year ended 31 March 1999

	1998/99 £'000	1997/98 £'000
Unrealised gain on revaluation of Land and Buildings	108	109
Unrealised loss on revaluation of other fixed assets	(1 278)	(76)
	(1 170)	33
Prior year adjustment for notional insurance	(472)	-
	(1 642)	33

The 1997/98 other operating costs and subsequent totals have been restated to reflect the removal of the National Insurance in accordance with FRS12, refer to note 1m.

Health and Safety Executive: Balance Sheet as at 31 March 1999

	Note	31 March 1999 £'000	£'000	Restated 31 March 1998 £'000	£'000
Fixed Assets					
Tangible assets	7		33 117		35 942
Current Assets					
Stocks	1i & 8	2 206		2 056	
Debtors	9	8 686		9 979	
Cash at bank and in hand	10	1 135		3 262	
		12 027		15 297	
Creditors (due within one year)	11	(7 663)		(9 036)	
Net Current Assets			4 364		6 261
Total Assets less Current Liabilities			37 481		42 203
Creditors (amounts falling due after more than one year)	11	(52)			(31)
Provisions for liabilities and charges	12	(3 005)	(3 057)		(3 000)
			34 424		39 172
Taxpayers' Equity					
Deferred Government Grants			49 372		52 676
Revaluation Reserve			1 780		1 724
Current Replacement Cost Reserve			2 060		1 922
General Fund			(18 788)		(17 150)
			34 424		39 172

The 1997/98 Reserves have been restated to reflect the removal of Notional Insurance in accordance with FRS12.

Health and Safety Executive: Cash Flow Statement year ended 31 March 1999

	Note	1998/99 £'000	Restated 1997/98 £'000
	Net Cash	(168 335)	(169 086)
Capital Expenditure and Financial Investment	14	(8 758)	(6 657)
Servicing of Finance		-	(373)
Payments to the Consolidated Fund	14	(1 986)	(670)
Financing from the Consolidated Fund		176 952	178 090
(Decrease)/Increase in Cash in the Period		(2 127)	1 304
Reconciliation of operating cost to operating cash flows			
Net Operating Cost	Schedule 2	181 113	176 299
Adjust for non-cash transactions		(14 331)	(10 235)
Adjust for movements in working capital other than cash		(1 758)	(1 156)
Adjust for transfer from provision		3 311	4 178
Net Cash Outflow from Operating Activities		168 335	169 086
Analysis of capital expenditure and financial investment			
Purchases of fixed assets		9 394	7 053
Proceeds of disposal of fixed assets		(636)	(396)
Net cash outflow from investing activities		8 758	6 657
Analysis of financing			
From Consolidated Fund		176 952	178 090
Decrease/(Increase) in Cash		2 127	(1 304)
Net Cash Requirement		179 079	176 786

Health and Safety Executive: Resources by Departmental Aims for year ended 31 March 1999

	1998/99			1997/98 restated		
	Gross £'000	Income £'000	Net £'000	Gross £'000	Income £'000	Net £'000
Aims/Objectives						
First Aim:						
To modernise, simplify and support the regulatory framework, including EU and other international work	38 557	(2 534)	36 023	36 563	(744)	35 819
Second Aim:						
To secure compliance with the law in line with the principles of proportionality, consistency, transparency and targeting on a risk related basis	114 366	(18 714)	95 652	115 471	(20 557)	94 914
Third Aim:						
To improve the knowledge and understanding of health and safety through the provision of appropriate (and timely) information and advice	27 388	(7 615)	19 773	25 523	(6 097)	19 426
Fourth Aim:						
To promote risk assessment and technical knowledge as the basis for setting standards and guiding enforcement activities	26 371	(959)	25 412	24 061	(1 029)	23 032
Fifth Aim:						
To operate statutory schemes, including regulatory services, through, for example, EMAS	9 366	(5 113)	4 253	7 883	(4 775)	3 108
Net Operating Costs	216 048	(34 935)	181 113	209 501	(33 202)	176 299

The 1997/98 other operating costs and subsequent totals have been restated to reflect the removal of the Notional Insurance in accordance with FRS12.

GLOSSARY OF ABBREVIATIONS (TO PART 1)

ACDP	Advisory Committee on Dangerous Pathogens
ACGM	Advisory Committee on Genetic Modification
ACoP	Approved Code of Practice
ACPO	Association of Chief Police Officers
ACTS	Advisory Committee on Toxic Substances
BOHS	British Occupational Hygiene Society
CCNSG	Client/Contractor National Safety Group
CDM	Construction (Design and Management) Regulations
CEN	Comite European de Normalisation (European standards committee)
CHID	Chemical and Hazardous Installations Division
CHIP	Chemical (Hazard Information and Packaging) Regulations
CHSW	Construction (Health, Safety and Welfare) Regulations
CIF	Chemical Industries Forum
COMAH	Control of Major Accident Hazards Regulations
COSHH	Control of Substances Hazardous to Health Regulations
CPS	Crown Prosecution Service
DAG	Direct Access Government
DETR	Department of Environment, Transport and the Regions
DST	Directorate of Science and Technology
DTI	Department of Trade and Industry
EECS	Electrical Equipment Certification Service
EEF	Engineering Employers' Federation
EMAS	Employment Medical Advisory Service
EU	European Union
FOD	Field Operations Directorate
GHGB	Good Health is Good Business
HAV	Hand-Arm Vibration
HD	Health Directorate
HELA	Health and Safety Executive/Local Authorities Enforcement Committee
HGV	Heavy Goods Vehicle
HSC	Health and Safety Commission
HSE	Health and Safety Executive
HSL	Health and Safety Laboratory
HSWA	Health and Safety at Work Act 1974
IAC	Industry Advisory Committee
IiP	Investors in People
IT	Information Technology

LAU	Local Authority Unit
LU	London Underground
MAFF	Ministry of Agriculture, Fisheries and Food
MI	Mines Inspectorate
NHS	National Health Service
OHAC	Occupational Health Advisory Committee
OSD	Offshore Safety Division
PPP	Public-Private Partnership
RAB	Resource Accounting and Budgeting
RI	Railway Inspectorate
RIDDOR	Reporting of Injuries, Diseases and Dangerous Occurrences Regulations
RoSPA	Royal Society for the Prevention of Accidents
SEPA	Scottish Environmental Protection Agency
SMEs	Small and Medium Sized Enterprises
SMSU	Senior Management Support Unit
SWI	Self-reported Work-related Illness Survey
TEC	Training and Enterprise Council
TUC	Trades Union Congress
UKAEA	United Kingdom Atomic Energy Authority
UN	United Nations
WCO	Workplace Contact Officer
WRULD	Work-Related Upper Limb Disorder
WTO	Working Time Officer

Printed in the UK for The Stationery Office Limited
on behalf of the Controller of Her Majesty's Stationery Office
Dd   /99   ,   , Ord